PRENTICE HALL

SCIENCE EXPLORER

Focus on
Physical Science
Teacher's Edition

Guided Reading and
Study Workbook

PRENTICE HALL
Needham, Massachusetts
Upper Saddle River, New Jersey
Glenview, Illinois

Teacher's Edition ISBN 0-13-052732-7

1 2 3 4 5 6 7 8 9 10   06 05 04 03 02 01 00

Table of Contents

© Prentice-Hall, Inc.

TABLE OF CONTENTS *(continued)*

CHAPTER 1

MOTION

. . . .

SECTION 1-1 ## Describing and Measuring Motion
(pages 6-17)

This section explains how to recognize when an object is in motion and how to determine how fast it is moving.

▶ Recognizing Motion (pages 7–8)

1. An object is in _____motion_____ when its distance from another object is changing.

2. What is a reference point? __A reference point is a place or object used for__ __comparison to determine if something is in motion.__

3. An object is in motion if it changes position relative to a(n) __reference__ __point__.

▶ Describing Distance (pages 8–9)

4. Complete the table about SI.

SI	
Question	**Answer**
What is its whole name?	International System of Units
What number is it based on?	Ten
What is its basic unit of length?	Meter

5. How many centimeters are there in a meter? _____100_____

6. How many meters are there in a kilometer? _____1,000_____

© Prentice-Hall, Inc.

CHAPTER 1, Motion *(continued)*

▶ Calculating Speed (pages 10–11)

7. What is the formula used to calculate the speed of an object?

   Speed = $\dfrac{\text{Distance}}{\text{Time}}$ _____

8. How would you find the average speed of a cyclist throughout an entire

   race? _Divide the total distance the cyclist traveled by the total time._

   _____

▶ Describing Velocity (pages 12–15)

9. Speed in a given direction is called ____velocity____.

10. An approaching storm is moving at 15 km/hr. What do you need to

    know to determine its velocity? _The direction in which it is moving_

    _____

▶ Graphing Motion (pages 15–17)

11. The steepness, or slant, of a line on a graph is called its ____slope____.

12. What is the formula used to find the slope of a line?

    Slope = $\dfrac{\text{rise}}{\text{run}}$ _____

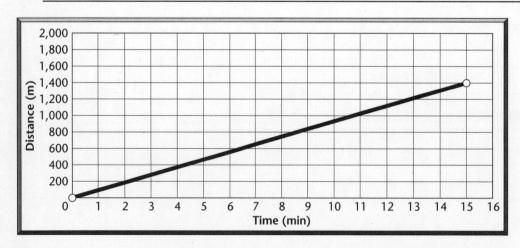

13. The motion graph above graphs the motion of a jogger on a run one

    day. How far did the jogger run in 15 minutes? ____1,400 m____

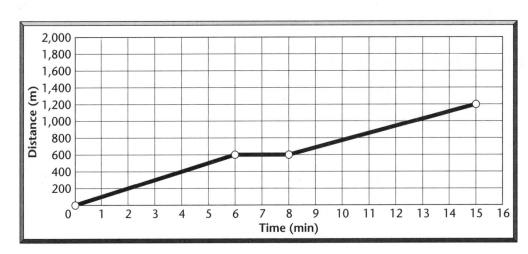

14. The motion graph above also shows the motion of a jogger on a run one day. The line is divided into segments. The middle segment is horizontal. What does that tell you about the jogger's progress between

minute 6 and minute 8? _The jogger traveled no distance during those_

minutes; the jogger rested.

_____

_____

SECTION 1-2 **Slow Motion on Planet Earth** (pages 20-23)

This section describes the movements of Earth's continents. It also gives a theory that explains why the continents move.

▶ What Are Earth's Plates? (pages 20–21)

1. Is the following sentence true or false? Earth's rocky outer shell is all one

piece. ____false____

2. The upper layer of Earth consists of more than a dozen major pieces

called ____plates____.

3. What is the theory of plate tectonics? _According to this theory, Earth's_

plates move ever so slowly in various directions.

_____

_____

CHAPTER 1, Motion *(continued)*

4. Circle the letter of each sentence that is true about Earth's plates.

    (**a.**)Some plates push toward each other.

    (**b.**)Some plates slide past each other.

    c. Earth consists of five major plates.

    (**d.**)Some plates pull away from each other.

▶ How Fast Do Plates Move? (pages 21–23)

5. Is the following sentence true or false? The speed of Earth's plates is very

    slow. _____ true _____

6. By knowing the average speed of a plate, what can scientists estimate

    about Earth's continents? __Scientists can estimate how the continents__

    moved in the past and how they may move in the future.
_____

7. What formula do scientists use to predict how far a plate will move in a
certain amount of time?

    Distance = Speed × Time
_____

8. Is the following sentence true or false? The shapes and positions of

    Earth's continents will not change in the future. _____ false _____

9. A conversion factor is a fraction in which the numerator and the

    denominator are _____ equal _____.

Reading Skill Practice

By looking carefully at photographs and illustrations in textbooks, you can help yourself
understand what you have read. Look carefully at Figure 10 on pages 22 and 23. What
important idea does this illustration communicate? Do your work on a separate sheet of paper.

The shapes and positions of Earth's continents have changed greatly over time and will
continue to change.

SECTION 1-3 Acceleration (pages 26-30)

This section describes what happens to the motion of an object as it accelerates, or changes velocity. It also explains how to calculate acceleration.

▶ Acceleration in Science (pages 26–28)

1. What is acceleration? Acceleration is the rate at which velocity changes.

   _____

2. Acceleration involves a change in what two components?
   speed and direction

3. Any time the speed of an object increases, the object experiences
   acceleration.

4. Is the following sentence true or false? Acceleration refers to increasing
   speed, decreasing speed, or changing direction. ____true____

5. Deceleration is another word for negative ____acceleration____.

6. Is the following sentence true or false? An object can be accelerating
   even if its speed is constant. ____true____

7. Circle the letter of each sentence that describes an example of
   acceleration.

   a. A car follows a gentle curve in the road.

   b. A batter swings a bat to hit a ball.

   c. A truck parked on a hill doesn't move all day.

   d. A runner slows down after finishing a race.

8. The moon revolves around Earth at a fairly constant speed. Is the moon
   accelerating? The moon is accelerating because it is constantly changing
   direction as it revolves around Earth.

CHAPTER 1, Motion *(continued)*

9. Use the table below to compare and contrast the meanings of *acceleration*.

Acceleration	
In Everyday Language	**In Scientific Language**
Speeding up	Increasing speed
	Decreasing speed
	Changing direction

▶ Calculating Acceleration (pages 28–30)

10. What must you calculate to determine the acceleration of an object?

The change in velocity during each unit of time

11. What is the formula you use to determine acceleration?

$$\text{Acceleration} = \frac{\text{Final velocity} - \text{Initial velocity}}{\text{Time}}$$

12. Is the following sentence true or false? To calculate the acceleration of an automobile, you must first subtract the final speed from the initial speed. _____ false _____

13. Circle the letter of each sentence that is true about calculating the acceleration of a moving object.

(**a.**) If an object is moving without changing direction, then its acceleration is the change in its speed during one unit of time.

(**b.**) If an object's speed changes by the same amount during each unit of time, then the acceleration of the object at any time is the same.

c. To determine the acceleration of an object, you must calculate the change in velocity during only one unit of time.

(**d.**) If an object's acceleration varies, then you can describe only average acceleration.

Science Explorer *Focus on Physical Science*

14. Suppose velocity is measured in kilometers/hour and time is measured

in hours. What is the unit of acceleration? _____ km/h² _____

▶ Graphing Acceleration (page 30)

15. If a graph of distance versus time is a straight line, the graph shows a(n)

_____ linear _____ relationship.

16. If a graph of distance versus time is a curved line, the graph shows a(n)

_____ nonlinear _____ relationship.

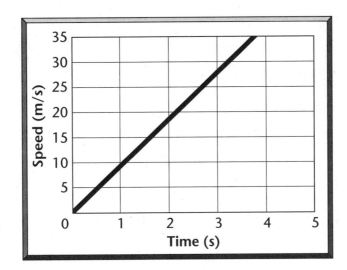

17. The graph above shows the motion of an object that is accelerating.

What happens to the speed of the object over time? _____ The speed increases _____

over time. _____

_____

18. The graph line is slanted and straight. What does this line show about

the acceleration of the object? _____ The acceleration is constant. _____

_____

_____

CHAPTER 1, Motion *(continued)*

WordWise

Match each definition in the left column with the correct term in the right column. Then write the number of each term in the appropriate box below. When you have filled in all the boxes, add up the numbers in each column, row, and two diagonals. All the sums should be the same.

A. When an object's distance from another object is changing

B. A place or object used for comparison to determine if something is in motion

C. The system of measurement scientists use to communicate information clearly

D. The basic SI unit of length

E. The distance an object travels in one unit of time

F. Speed in a given direction

G. The steepness, or slant, of a line on a graph

H. The major pieces of Earth's crust

I. The rate at which velocity changes

1. reference point

2. slope

3. velocity

4. acceleration

5. speed

6. motion

7. meter

8. International System of Units (SI)

9. plates

= _____15_____

A 6	B 1	C 8	= _____15_____
D 7	E 5	F 3	= _____15_____
G 2	H 9	I 4	= _____15_____
= 15	= 15	= 15	= _____15_____

Science Explorer *Focus on Physical Science*

MathWise

For the problems below, show your calculations. If you need more space, use another sheet of paper. Write the answers for the problems on the lines below.

▶ Calculating Speed (pages 10–11)

1. Speed $= \dfrac{32 \text{ m}}{8 \text{ s}} =$ ___4 m/s___

2. A car travels 66 kilometers in 3 hours. What is its speed?

   Speed $= \dfrac{66 \text{ km}}{3 \text{ hr}} = 22$ km/hr

   Answer: ___Speed = 22 km/hr___

▶ Average Speed (page 11)

3. Average Speed $= \dfrac{200 \text{ km}}{5 \text{ hr}} =$ ___40 km/hr___

4. Suppose a car travels 60 kilometers the first two hours and 15 kilometers the next hour. What is the car's average speed?

   Average speed $= \dfrac{75 \text{ km}}{3 \text{ hr}} = 25$ km/hr

   Answer: ___Average speed = 25 km/hr___

▶ Calculating Slope (page 16)

5. Slope $= \dfrac{20 \text{ m} - 5 \text{ m}}{9 \text{ s} - 6 \text{ s}} =$ ___5 m/s___

6. A line in a graph has a constant slope. The rise of the line is 15 meters, while the run of the line 3 seconds. What is the slope of the line?

   Slope $= \dfrac{15 \text{ m}}{3 \text{ s}} = 5$ m/s

   Answer: ___Slope = 5 m/s___

CHAPTER 1, Motion *(continued)*

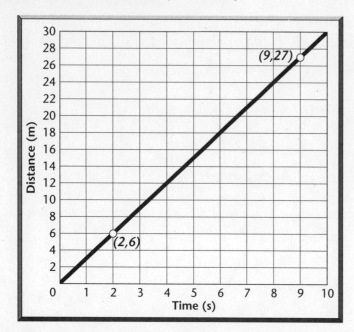

7. Two points on the line graph above are (9, 27) and (2, 6). What is the slope of the line?

Slope = $\dfrac{27\ m - 6\ m}{9\ s - 2\ s}$ = $\dfrac{21\ m}{7\ s}$ = 3 m/s

Answer: _____ Slope = 3 m/s _____

▶ Calculating Distance (pages 21–22)

8. Distance = $\dfrac{7\ cm}{1\ yr}$ × 1,000 yr = ___7,000 cm___

9. Suppose one of Earth's plates moved 4 cm over the course of a year. How far will it move in 500 years?

Distance = $\dfrac{4\ cm}{1\ yr}$ × 500 yr = 2,000 cm

Answer: _____ Distance = 2,000 cm _____

▶ Calculating Acceleration (pages 28–30)

11. Acceleration = $\dfrac{20\ m/s - 4\ m/s}{4\ s}$ = ___4 m/s²___

12. A cheetah accelerates from 2 m/s to 16 m/s in 7 seconds. What is the cheetah's average acceleration?

Acceleration = $\dfrac{16\ m/s - 2\ m/s}{7\ s}$ = 2 m/s²

Answer: _____ Acceleration = 2 m/s² _____

Science Explorer *Focus on Physical Science*

CHAPTER 2

FORCES

· ·

SECTION 2-1 ### The Nature of Force
(pages 36-41)

This section explains how balanced and unbalanced forces are related to motion. It also explains Newton's first law of motion.

▶ **What Is Force?** (pages 36–37)

1. In science, a force is __a push or a pull_____.

2. When one object pushes or pulls another object, the first object is _____exerting_____ a force on the second object.

3. Circle the letters of the two ways that forces are described.

   (a.) direction   **b.** velocity   **(c.)** strength   **d.** acceleration

▶ **Unbalanced Forces** (pages 37–38)

4. When two forces act in the same direction, they _____add_____ together.

5. Adding a force acting in one direction to a force acting in another direction is the same as adding a(n) _____positive_____ number and a(n) _____negative_____ number.

6. Look at Figure 1 on page 37. What does the width of the arrows tell you about the forces they represent? __The width of each arrow tells you the strength of a force. A wider arrow shows greater force.__

7. The overall force on an object after all the forces are added together is called the _____net force_____.

CHAPTER 2, Forces (continued)

8. The illustrations to the right represent ways that two forces can combine. Draw lines from the left column to the right column to show the result of each combination.

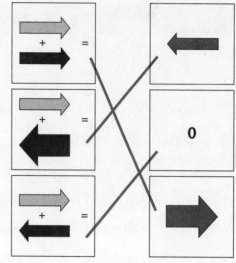

9. Unbalanced forces can cause an object to do three things. What are they?

   Start moving, stop moving, or change direction

10. Is the following sentence true or false? Unbalanced forces acting on an object will change the object's motion. _____true_____

11. Circle the letter of each sentence that is true about unbalanced forces.

   a. When two forces act in opposite directions, the net force is the difference between the two forces.

   b. When two forces act in the same direction, the net force is the difference between the two forces.

   c. When two forces act in opposite directions, the net force is equal to the greater force.

   d. When two forces act in the same direction, the net force is the sum of the two individual forces.

▶ Balanced Forces (pages 38–39)

12. Equal forces acting on one object in opposite directions are called

   _____balanced forces_____.

© Prentice-Hall, Inc.

13. Is the following sentence true or false? Balanced forces acting on an object will change the object's motion. _____false_____

14. When you add equal forces exerted in opposite directions, the net force is _____zero_____.

▶ Newton's First Law of Motion (pages 40–41)

15. For an object to stay in motion, a(n) _____force_____ has to act on it.

16. Is the following sentence true or false? Once an object is in its natural resting place, it cannot move by itself. _____true_____

17. What is inertia? __Inertia is the tendency of an object to resist change in its__ motion.

18. What is Newton's first law of motion? __An object at rest will remain at__ rest, and an object that is moving at constant velocity will continue moving at constant velocity unless acted upon by an unbalanced force.

19. Newton's first law of motion is also called the law of _____inertia_____.

20. What explains why you continue moving forward if you are in a car that suddenly stops? _____inertia_____

21. What is mass? __Mass is the amount of matter in an object.__

22. What is the SI unit of mass? __the kilogram, or kg__

23. The amount of inertia an object has depends on its _____mass_____.

24. How can mass be defined in terms of inertia? __Mass can be defined as__ a measure of the inertia of an object.

CHAPTER 2, Forces (continued)

• •

SECTION 2-2 Force, Mass, and Acceleration
(pages 44-46)

This section explains how force and mass are related to acceleration.

▶ **Newton's Second Law of Motion** (pages 44–45)

1. What is Newton's second law of motion? __The net force on an object is__

   equal to the product of its acceleration and its mass.

2. What is the equation that describes the relationship among quantities of force, mass, and acceleration?

   Force = Mass × Acceleration

3. Circle the letters of the two answers below that are different names for the same unit of measure.

   a. m/s^2 **(b.)** N   **(c.)** kg • ms^2 **d.** 1 kg

4. What equation for Newton's second law can you use to find acceleration?

   Acceleration = $\dfrac{\text{Force}}{\text{Mass}}$

▶ **Changes in Force and Mass** (page 46)

5. How does an increase of force affect acceleration? __An increase of force__

   increases acceleration.

6. What are two ways you can increase the acceleration of an object?

   You can increase the force or decrease the mass of the object.

7. How does an increase of mass affect acceleration? <u>An increase of mass</u>
<u>decreases acceleration.</u>

8. Is the following sentence true or false? One way to increase the force used to pull a wagon is to decrease the mass in the wagon.
<u>true</u>

. . . .

SECTION 2-3 Friction and Gravity (pages 47-53)

This section describes the effects of friction on surfaces that rub on each other. It also describes how gravity acts between objects in the universe.

▶ Friction (pages 48–49)

1. Is the following sentence true or false? When two surfaces rub, the irregularities of one surface get caught on those of the other surface.
<u>true</u>

2. What is friction? <u>Friction is the force that one surface exerts on another</u>
<u>when the two rub against each other.</u>

3. Friction acts in a direction <u>opposite</u> to the object's direction of motion.

4. The strength of the force of friction depends on what two factors?
<u>The types of surfaces involved and how hard the surfaces push together</u>

5. How is friction useful in helping you walk? <u>Friction acts between the</u>
<u>soles of your shoes and the floor. Without friction, your shoes would only</u>
<u>slide across the floor, and you would never move forward.</u>

CHAPTER 2, Forces *(continued)*

6. How does friction help an automobile move? _An automobile moves_

because of friction between its tires and the road.

_____

7. Complete the following table about the different kinds of friction.

Kinds of Friction	
Kind of Friction	**Friction Occurs When . . .**
Fluid friction	An object moves through a fluid
Sliding friction	Solid surfaces slide over each other
Rolling friction	An object rolls over a surface

8. Which kind of friction requires more force to overcome, rolling friction or sliding friction? _sliding friction_

9. What kind of friction occurs when moving parts have ball bearings? _rolling friction_

10. How does oil between machine parts reduce friction? _The oil keeps the_ _machine parts from making direct contact, and there is fluid friction between_ _the parts instead of sliding friction._

▶ Gravity (pages 50–52)

11. The force that pulls objects toward Earth is called _gravity_ .

12. When is an object said to be in free fall? _An object is in free fall when_ _the only force acting on the falling object is gravity._

13. Near the surface of Earth, what is the acceleration of an object due to the force of gravity? _9.8 m/s^2_

14. An object that is thrown is called a(n) _projectile_ .

15. Is the following sentence true or false? An object that is dropped will hit the ground before an object that is thrown horizontally. ____false____

16. Objects falling through air experience a type of fluid friction called ____air resistance____.

17. Is the following sentence true or false? The greater the surface area of an object, the greater the air resistance. ____true____

18. On the diagram below, draw arrows that show the forces acting on the falling acorn. Label each arrow with the name of the force.

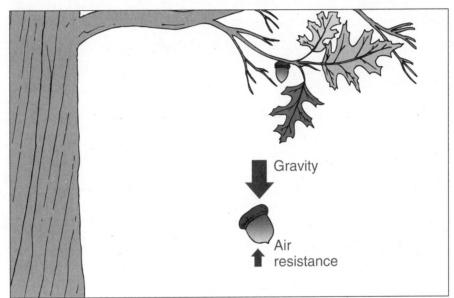

19. The greatest velocity a falling object reaches is called ____terminal velocity____.

20. What is weight? __Weight is the force of gravity on a person or object at the surface of a planet.__

21. How is weight different than mass? __Weight is a measure of the force of gravity on an object, while mass is a measure of the amount of matter in an object.__

22. Weight is usually measured in ____newtons____.

CHAPTER 2, Forces *(continued)*

▶ Universal Gravitation (pages 52–53)

23. Is the following sentence true or false? The force that makes an apple fall to the ground is the same force that keeps Earth orbiting the sun.

_____true_____

24. What does the universal law of gravitation state? _____The force of gravity_____

acts between all objects in the universe.

_____

25. Is the following sentence true or false? On the moon, your mass would be less than it is on Earth, but your weight would be the same.

_____false_____

26. The force of attraction between two objects varies with what two

factors? ___Mass and the square of the distance between the objects___

_____

· ·

SECTION 2-4 Action and Reaction (pages 56-61)

This section explains Newton's third law of motion. It also explains a law about moving objects.

▶ Newton's Third Law of Motion (pages 56–58)

1. What is Newton's third law of motion? ___If one object exerts a force on___

another object, then the second object exerts a force of equal magnitude in

the opposite direction on the first object.

_____

2. What did Newton call the force exerted by the first object on a second

object? _____action force_____

© Prentice-Hall, Inc.

3. What did Newton call the force exerted by the second object back on

the first object? _____reaction force_____

4. The action and reaction forces in any situation will always be

_____equal_____ and _____opposite_____ .

5. Complete the flowchart below, which describes how a squid moves
through water.

Newton's Squid

A squid expels water out its back end. This is the

_____action_____ force.

↓

The water expelled out of the back end of the squid pushes

back, exerting an equal and _____opposite_____ force

on the squid. This is the _____reaction_____ force.

↓

The squid moves _____ahead_____ through the

water as a result of the reaction force.

6. Explain why the equal action and reaction forces do not cancel each

other when one person hits a ball. _____Forces can be added together only if_____

they are acting on the same object. When one person hits a ball, the action

force is exerted on the ball, while the equal reaction force is exerted back on

the person. Therefore, the equal forces in this situation cannot be added

together and do not cancel each other.

CHAPTER 2, Forces *(continued)*

▶ Momentum (page 58)

7. The product of an object's mass and velocity is its ___momentum___ .

8. What is the equation you use to determine the momentum of an object?
   Momentum = Mass × Velocity

9. What is the unit of measurement for momentum? ___kilogram-meters per___
   second, kg • m/s

▶ Conservation of Momentum (pages 60–61)

10. What does the law of conservation of momentum state? ___The total___
    momentum of the objects that interact does not change.

11. Suppose a train car moving down a track at 10 m/s hits another train
    car that is not moving. Explain how momentum is conserved after the
    collision. ___The result of the collision is that the first train car stops and the___
    second train car moves forward at 10 m/s. In that case, the momentum of
    the first train car is transferred to the second train car.

 Reading Skill Practice

A flowchart can help you remember the order in which a series of events occurs. Create a
flowchart that describes how momentum is conserved when a moving train car collides with
another moving train car. See your textbook on page 60. The first step in the flowchart will be
this: One train car moves down a track at 10 m/s. The last step in the flowchart will be this:
Momentum is conserved. Do your work on a separate sheet of paper. For more information
about flowcharts, see page 833 in the Skills Handbook of your textbook.

Students' flowcharts will vary. A typical flowchart might include these steps: One train car
moves down a track at 10 m/s. The first train car collides with another train car, which is moving
in the same direction at 5 m/s. During the collision, the first train car slows down to 5 m/s, and
the second train car speeds up to 10 m/s. Momentum is conserved.

Science Explorer *Focus on Physical Science*

● ●

SECTION 2-5 **Orbiting Satellites**
(pages 62-64)

This section explains how a rocket lifts off the ground and what keeps an object in orbit.

▶ **How Do Rockets Lift Off?** (pages 62–63)

1. Which of Newton's laws explains the lifting of a rocket into space?
   Newton's third law of motion
   _____

2. When a rocket rises, what causes the action force? A downward force is
   caused as the rocket expels exhaust gases.
   _____

3. When a rocket rises, what causes the reaction force? The gases forced
   out of the rocket exert a force equal in magnitude but opposite in direction on
   the rocket.
   _____

4. On the diagram of a rocket lifting off the ground, draw and label arrows that show the action force and the reaction force.

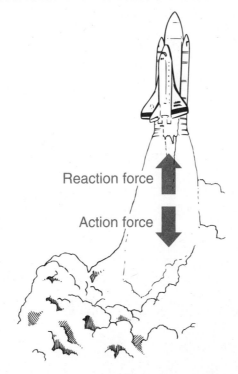

Reaction force

Action force

CHAPTER 2, Forces *(continued)*

5. When a rocket lifts off the ground, the net force is in an upward direction. Is the upward pushing force greater or lesser than the downward pull of gravity? _____ greater _____

▶ What Is a Satellite? (pages 63–64)

6. Any object that travels around another object in space is a(n) _____ satellite _____.

7. An object traveling in a circle is accelerating because it is constantly changing _____ direction _____.

8. What is a force called that causes an object to move in a circle? _____ a centripetal force _____

9. For a satellite, what is the centripetal force that causes it to move in a circle? _____ gravitational force _____

10. Is the following sentence true or false? Satellites in orbit around Earth continually fall toward Earth. _____ true _____

11. Explain why a satellite in orbit around Earth does not fall into Earth.
    The satellite does not fall into Earth because Earth is curved. As a result,
    the satellite falls around Earth rather than into it.

12. A satellite is a projectile that falls _____ around _____ Earth rather than into Earth.

13. Why doesn't a satellite need fuel to keep orbiting? _____ A satellite continues
    to move ahead due to its inertia.

14. What force continually changes a satellite's direction? _____ gravity _____

WordWise

Use the clues to help you find the key terms from Chapter 2 hidden in the puzzle below. The terms may occur vertically, horizontally, or diagonally.

1. A _____force_____ is a push or pull.

2. The overall force on an object after all forces are added together is called the _____net_____ force.

3. The tendency of an object to resist change in its motion is called _____inertia_____.

4. The amount of matter in an object is called _____mass_____.

5. One _____newton_____ equals the force required to accelerate 1 kilogram of mass at 1 meter per second per second.

6. The force that one surface exerts on another when the two rub against each other is called _____friction_____.

7. When solid surfaces slide over each other, the kind of friction that occurs is _____sliding_____ friction.

8. The friction that occurs when an object moves through a fluid is called _____fluid_____ friction.

9. The force that pulls objects toward Earth is _____gravity_____.

10. When the only force acting on a falling object is gravity, the object is said to be in _____free_____ fall.

11. Objects falling through air experience a type of fluid friction called _____air_____ resistance.

12. The force of gravity on a person or object at the surface of a planet is known as _____weight_____.

13. The _____momentum_____ of an object is the product of its mass and velocity.

14. Any object that travels around another object in space is a(n) _____satellite_____.

```
m   q   m   o   m   e   n   t   u   m
a   f   g   i   n   e   r   t   i   a
s   o   r   l   i   o   l   n   g   f
s   r   a   i   q   a   z   y   n   r
w   c   v   p   c   f   r   e   e   i
w   e   i   g   h   t   a   e   w   c
u   p   t   f   l   u   i   d   t   t
i   e   y   c   n   i   r   o   o   i
n   s   l   i   d   i   n   g   n   o
s   a   t   e   l   l   i   t   e   n
```

CHAPTER 2, Forces *(continued)*

MathWise

For the problems below, show your calculations. If you need more space, use another sheet of paper. Write the answers for the problems on the lines below.

▶ **Newton's Second Law of Motion** (pages 44–45)

1. Force = 65 kg × 3ms² = ____195 N____

2. A 250-kg trailer is being pulled by a truck. The force causes the trailer to accelerate at 4 m/s². What is the net force that causes this acceleration?

   Force = 250 kg × 4 m/s² = 1,000 N

   Answer: ____Force = 1,000 N____

▶ **Weight and Mass** (pages 51–52)

3. Weight = 45 kg × 9.8 m/s² = ____441 N____

4. What is the weight of a rock that has a mass of 7 kg?

   Weight = 7 kg × 9.8 m/s² = 68.6 N

   Answer: ____Weight = 68.6 N____

▶ **Momentum** (page 59)

5. Momentum = 5 kg × 6.5 m/s = ____32.5 kg • m/s____

6. A baseball travels at 7 m/s, while a basketball moves at 3 m/s. The mass of the baseball is 0.14 kg and the mass of the basketball is 0.5 kg. Which has the greater momentum? ____The baseball's momentum is 0.98 kg • m/s,____ while the basketball's momentum is 1.5 kg • m/s. Thus, the basketball has the greater momentum.

CHAPTER 3

FORCES IN FLUIDS

● ●

SECTION 3-1 **Pressure** (pages 70-75)

This section explains what causes pressure in fluids. It also describes how pressure changes with altitude and depth.

▶ What Is Pressure? (pages 70–72)

1. What do snowshoes do that makes it easier for the person wearing them to travel in deep snow? Snowshoes distribute a person's weight over the large area of the snowshoes, resulting in less downward pressure on the snow compared to regular shoes. With less downward pressure, the person doesn't sink into the snow.

2. Is the following sentence true or false? Force and pressure are the same thing. ___false___

3. What is pressure equal to? The force exerted on a surface divided by the total area over which the force is exerted

4. Circle the letter of the term that is an SI unit of pressure.
   a. newton   **b.** liter   **c.** weight   **d.** pascal

5. Circle the letter of the *two* answers below that are equal to each other.
   a. 1 Pa   **b.** 1 N/cm^2 **c.** 1 N/m^2 **d.** 1 N

6. What unit of measure is used when a smaller unit is more practical for an area? N/cm^2

© Prentice-Hall, Inc.

CHAPTER 3, Forces in Fluids *(continued)*

7. Is the following sentence true or false? You can produce a lower

   pressure by decreasing the area a force acts on. _____false_____

▶ Fluid Pressure (page 72)

8. A substance that can easily flow is a(n) _____fluid_____.

9. Circle the letter of each of the following that are fluids.

   (a.) helium gas   (b.) liquid water   c. ice   (d.) air

10. Describe how molecules move in fluids. __In fluids, molecules are__

    __constantly moving in all directions. They are constantly colliding with each__

    __other and with any surface that they meet.__

    _____

11. What causes the pressure exerted by a fluid? __All of the forces exerted by__

    __the individual molecules in a fluid add together to make up the pressure__

    __exerted by the fluid.__

    _____

12. The pressure exerted by a fluid is the total force exerted by the fluid

    divided by the _____area_____ over which the force is exerted.

▶ Fluid Pressure All Around (page 73)

13. What is another term for air pressure? __atmospheric pressure__

14. What causes air pressure? __The force of gravity on air's mass produces air__

    __pressure.__

▶ Balanced Pressures (pages 73–74)

15. Is the following sentence true or false? In a fluid that is not moving,
    pressure at a given point is exerted equally in all directions.

    _____true_____

© Prentice-Hall, Inc.

16. On the illustration of the hand, draw arrows that indicate where the atmosphere is exerting air pressure on the hand. The size of each arrow should indicate the amount of air pressure on that part of the hand.

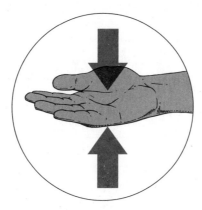

▶ Variations in Fluid Pressure (pages 74–75)

17. Is the following sentence true or false? Air pressure increases as

elevation increases. _____ false _____

18. Why is air pressure lower at a higher elevation than at a lower elevation?

At the higher elevation, there is less air above and therefore less weight of

air to support than at a lower elevation.

_____

_____

19. Is the following sentence true or false? Water pressure increases as

depth increases. _____ true _____

20. Why is water pressure greater at a greater depth than at a shallow depth?

At a greater depth, there is more water above than there is at a shallow

depth.

_____

21. The total pressure at a given point beneath the water results from the

weight of the water above plus the weight of the _____ air _____

above it.

CHAPTER 3, Forces in Fluids *(continued)*

 Reading Skill Practice

Writing a summary can help you remember the information you have read. When you write a summary, write only the important points. Write a summary of the information under the heading *Fluid Pressure,* page 72. Your summary should be shorter than the text on which it is based. Do your work on a separate sheet of paper.

Students' summaries will vary, though all should include the definition of *fluid* and the highlighted sentence in the fourth paragraph.

. . . .

SECTION 3-2 **Transmitting Pressure in a Fluid**
(pages 78-81)

This section explains what Pascal's principle says about an increase in fluid pressure and describes how a hydraulic device works.

▶ **Pascal's Principle** (page 79)

1. What happens to the pressure in a bottle of water if you press the

   stopper at the top down farther? The pressure in the water increases

   everywhere in the bottle.

   _____

2. What is the relationship known as Pascal's principle? When force is

   applied to a confined fluid, an increase in pressure is transmitted equally to

   all parts of the fluid.

   _____

▶ **Force Pumps** (page 79)

3. What does a force pump do? It causes a fluid to move from one place to

   another by increasing the pressure in the fluid.

   _____

Science Explorer *Focus on Physical Science*

4. Describe the heart in terms of force pumps. The heart consists of two

force pumps. One pumps blood to the lungs, and the other pumps blood to

the rest of the body.

▶ Using Pascal's Principle (pages 80–81)

5. Suppose you push down on a small piston that is connected to a confined fluid, and another piston with the same area is connected by a U-shaped tube to the confined fluid. How much fluid pressure will the second piston experience compared to the first? Both pistons will

experience the same fluid pressure.

6. Suppose you push down on a small piston that is connected to a confined fluid, and a piston twenty times larger is connected by a U-shaped tube to the confined fluid. How much fluid pressure will the larger piston experience compared to the small piston? The larger

piston will experience a fluid pressure twenty times larger.

7. In a hydraulic system, how is the force applied on a small surface area multiplied? The increase in pressure on a small surface area is

transmitted to another part of a confined fluid, which pushes on a larger

surface area.

8. Is the following sentence true or false? A car's brake system multiples the force of the driver's tap on the brake pedal. _____ true

9. The tube feet of a sea star take advantage of what principle to move around? _____ Pascal's principle

10. When a sea star contracts different muscles, it changes the _____ pressure _____ in the fluid of its tube foot.

11. The _____ pressure _____ a sea star exerts on the fluid in its system causes the tube foot to either push down or pull up on its sucker.

CHAPTER 3, Forces in Fluids *(continued)*

· ·

SECTION 3-3 # Floating and Sinking
(pages 82-88)

This section describes a force that acts on objects under water. It also explains why some objects float and others sink.

▶ **Buoyancy** (page 83)

1. Water exerts a(n) _____buoyant_____ force that acts on a submerged object.

2. Circle the letter of each sentence that is true about a buoyant force.

   (a.)It acts against the force of gravity.   (b.)It acts in an upward direction.

   c. It makes an object feel heavier.   (d.)It makes an object feel lighter.

3. How much fluid does a submerged object displace? __It displaces a__

   volume of fluid equal to the object's own volume. _____

   _____

4. What does the Archimedes' principle state? __The buoyant force on an__

   object is equal to the weight of the fluid displaced by the object. _____

   _____

▶ **Floating and Sinking** (page 86)

5. Is the following sentence true or false? If the weight of a submerged object is less than the buoyant force, the object will sink.

   _____false_____

6. What happens when the weight of a submerged object is exactly equal to

   the buoyant force? __The object will stop sinking deeper and will float.__

   _____

   _____

▶ Density (pages 86–88)

7. The _____density_____ of a substance, no matter what state or shape, is its mass per unit volume.

8. What formula do you use to find density? ___ $Density = \dfrac{Mass}{Volume}$ ___

9. What is the density of water? ___ 1.00 g/cm³ ___

b

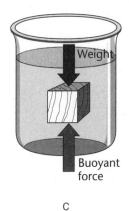

a

c

10. The illustrations above show three objects in water. All three objects are equal in volume. The captions for these illustrations are listed below. Write the letter of the correct caption under each illustration.

   a. Object is more dense than water.

   b. Object is less dense than water.

   c. Object has a density that is equal to water's density.

11. Is the following sentence true or false? An object that is more dense than the fluid in which it is immersed floats to the surface.

   _____false_____

12. An object that is _____more_____ dense than the fluid in which it is immersed sinks.

13. Figure 16 on page 87 shows the densities of several substances. Use the figure to rank the following substances, from 1 for least dense to 3 for most dense.

   ___3___ a. corn syrup   ___1___ b. wood   ___2___ c. plastic

CHAPTER 3, Forces in Fluids *(continued)*

14. Why does a helium balloon rise in air while an ordinary balloon filled with air does not? __Helium is less dense than air, and objects float in air if__ __their densities are less than air's density. A balloon filled with air does not__ __rise because the density of the air inside the balloon is not less than air's__ __density.__

15. When a submarine pumps water out of its floatation tanks, its density decreases and it floats. Why does its density decrease? __By pumping__ __water out, the submarine's overall mass decreases. Since its volume__ __remains the same, its density decreases when its mass decreases.__

16. Usually, the hull of a ship contains a large volume or air. Why? __The air reduces the ship's overall density, and so allows it to float.__

17. The amount of fluid displaced by a submerged object depends on its ____volume____.

18. A ship stays afloat as long as the ____buoyant____ force is greater than its weight.

© Prentice-Hall, Inc.

SECTION 3-4 Applying Bernoulli's Principle
(pages 89-92)

This section explains how the pressure of a fluid is related to the motion of the fluid.

▶ Bernoulli's Principle (pages 89-90)

1. Is the following sentence true or false? The faster a fluid moves, the more pressure the fluid exerts. ____false____

2. What does Bernoulli's principle state? _The pressure exerted by a moving_

stream of fluid is less than the pressure of the surrounding fluid.

_____

3. Is the following sentence true or false? A faster-moving fluid exerts less

pressure than a slower-moving fluid. ____true____

4. Explain why a sheet of tissue paper rises when you blow air above the

tissue paper. _The moving air above the tissue paper exerts less pressure_

than the still air below the paper. The greater pressure below the paper

pushes it upward.

▶ Objects in Flight (pages 90–91)

5. Is the following sentence true or false? Objects can be designed so that
their shapes cause air to move at different speeds above and below them.

____true____

6. If the air moves faster above an object, does pressure push the object

upward or downward? ____upward____

7. If the air moves faster below an object, does pressure push the object

upward or downward? ____downward____

8. On the illustration of a wing below, draw arrows that show the path of
air above and below the wing.

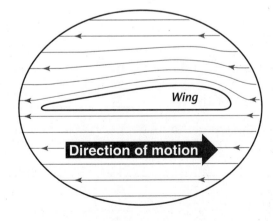

CHAPTER 3, Forces in Fluids *(continued)*

9. Air that moves over the top of an airplane wing must travel farther than air that moves along the bottom of the wing. As a result, the air moving over the top exerts less _____pressure_____ than the air moving along the bottom.

10. What is lift? __Lift is an upward force on a wing created by a difference in__ __pressure.__

11. In what way is an airplane wing shaped like a bird's wing? __Both are__ __curved on top.__

12. Why is a spoiler on a racing car curved on the lower side? __The spoiler__ __is shaped so that there is greater pressure pushing downward, which gives__ __the car traction from its rear wheels.__

▶ **Bernoulli's Principle at Home** (pages 90–92)

13. How do differences in air pressure cause smoke to rise up a chimney? __Wind blowing across the top of a chimney lowers the air pressure there. The__ __higher pressure at the bottom then pushes air and smoke up the chimney.__

14. Is the following sentence true or false? The moving water of a shower causes greater air pressure inside the shower curtain than outside the curtain. _____false_____

15. When you squeeze the rubber bulb of a perfume atomizer, how do you change the air pressure at the top of the tube? __Squeezing the bulb__ __causes air to move quickly past the top of the tube. The moving air lowers__ __the air pressure at the top of the tube.__

© Prentice-Hall, Inc.

WordWise

Answer the questions by writing the correct key terms in the blanks. Use the circled letter in each term to find the hidden key term. Then write a definition for the hidden key term.

1. Whose principle states that when force is applied to a confined fluid, an increase in pressure is transmitted equally to all parts of the fluid?

   (P) a   s   c   a   l

2. What is the force that acts in an upward direction, against the force of gravity, so it makes an object feel lighter?

   b   u   o   y   a   n   t   f   o   (r)   c   e

3. What kind of system multiplies by transmitting pressure to another part of a confined fluid?

   h   y   d   r   a   u   l   i   c   s   y   s   t   (e)   m

4. What is the unit of pressure equal to N/m²?

   p   a   (s)   c   a   l

5. What is the measurement of how much mass of a substance is contained in a unit of volume?

   d   e   n   (s)   i   t   y

6. What is a substance that can easily flow?

   f   l   (u)   i   d

7. Whose principle states that the buoyant force on an object is equal to the weight of the fluid displaced by the object?

   A   (r)   c   h   i   m   e   d   e   s

8. Whose principle states that the pressure exerted by a moving stream of fluid is less than the pressure of the surrounding fluid?

   B   (e)   r   n   o   u   l   l   i

Key Term: P   r   e   s   s   u   r   e

Definition: _Pressure is equal to the force exerted on a surface divided by the_ _total area over which the force is exerted._

CHAPTER 3, Forces in Fluids *(continued)*

MathWise

For the problems below, show your calculations. If you need more space, use another sheet of paper. Write the answers for the problems on the lines below.

▶ Calculating Pressure (pages 71–72)

1. Pressure = $\dfrac{20\ N}{10\ m^2}$ = _____ 2 Pa _____

2. A force of 25 N is exerted on a surface with an area of 5 m². What is the pressure on that area?

   Pressure = $\dfrac{25\ N}{5\ m^2}$ = 5 Pa

   Answer: _____ Pressure = 5 Pa _____

3. A force of 160 N is exerted on a surface with an area of 40 m². What is the pressure on that area?

   Pressure = $\dfrac{160\ N}{40\ m^2}$ = 4 Pa

   Answer: _____ Pressure = 4 Pa _____

▶ Density (pages 86–87)

4. Density = $\dfrac{12\ g}{3\ cm^3}$ = _____ 4 g/cm³ _____

5. A substance has a mass of 30 g and a volume of 15 cm³. What is its density?

   Density = $\dfrac{30\ g}{15\ cm^3}$ = 2 g/cm³

   Answer: _____ Density = 2 g/cm³ _____

6. A substance has a volume of 20 cm³ and a mass of 10 g. What is its density?

   Density = $\dfrac{10\ g}{20\ cm^3}$ = 1/2 g/cm³ = 0.5 g/cm³

   Answer: _____ Density = 0.5 g/cm³ _____

CHAPTER 4

WORK AND MACHINES

What Is Work?
(pages 98-101)

This section explains the scientific meaning of work and describes how to calculate the work done on an object.

▶ The Meaning of Work (pages 98–100)

1. In scientific terms, when do you do work? You do work when you exert a

   force on an object that causes the object to move some distance.

   _____

   _____

2. Complete the following table by classifying each example as either work or no work.

Work?	
Example	**Work or No Work?**
You pull your books out of your book bag.	work
You lift a bin of newspapers.	work
You push on a car stuck in the snow.	work
You hold a heavy piece of wood in place.	no work
You pull a sled through the snow.	work
You hold a bag of groceries.	no work

3. In order for you to do work on an object, the object must move some

   _____ distance _____ as a result of your force.

CHAPTER 4, Work and Machines (continued)

4. Explain why you don't do any work when you carry an object at a constant velocity. _In carrying an object, you exert an upward force. But to do work, you must exert a force in the same direction as the object's motion. Since the object's motion is horizontal and the force exerted is vertical, no work is done._

5. When you pull a sled through the snow, why does only part of your force do work? _When you pull a sled, you pull on the rope at an angle to the ground. Your force has a horizontal part and a vertical part. Only the horizontal part does work because that force is in the same direction as the motion of the sled._

▶ Calculating Work (pages 100–101)

6. The amount of work you do depends on both the amount of _____force_____ you exert and the _____distance_____ the object moves.

7. Is the following sentence true or false? Lifting a heavier object demands greater force than lifting a lighter object. _____true_____

8. Is the following sentence true or false? Moving an object a shorter distance requires more work than moving an object a greater distance. _____false_____

9. What formula do you use to determine the amount of work done on an object? _Work = Force × Distance_

10. What is the SI unit of work? _____joule_____

11. What is the amount of work you do when you exert a force of 1 newton to move an object a distance of 1 meter? _____1 joule_____

SECTION 4-2 Mechanical Advantage and Efficiency (pages 102-107)

This section explains how machines make work easier and describes how to calculate how efficient a machine is.

▶ What Is a Machine? (pages 102–104)

1. What is a machine? __A machine is a device with which you can do work in__ __a way that is easier or more effective.__ _____

2. Is the following sentence true or false? A machine decreases the amount of work needed to do a job. ___false___

3. Circle the letter of the sentences that are true about how a machine makes work easier.

   (a.) A machine makes work easier by multiplying force you exert.

   b. A machine makes work easier by reducing the amount of force needed to do the job.

   (c.) A machine makes work easier by multiplying the distance over which you exert force.

   (d.) A machine makes work easier by changing the direction in which you exert force.

4. The force you exert on a machine is called the ___input force___.

5. The force exerted by the machine is called the ___output force___.

6. Is the following sentence true or false? In some machines, the output force is greater than the input force. ___true___

7. If a machine allows you to use less force to do some amount of work, then you must apply the input force over a greater ___distance___.

8. Is the following sentence true or false? In some machines, the output force is less than the input force. ___true___

CHAPTER 4, Work and Machines *(continued)*

9. Write labels on the illustration below to show which arrow represents the input force and which represents the output force.

Input force   Output force

▶ Mechanical Advantage (page 105)

10. What is a machine's mechanical advantage? __The number of times a__

__force exerted on a machine is multiplied by the machine__

_____

11. What is the formula you use to determine the mechanical advantage of a machine?

$$\text{Mechanical advantage} = \frac{\text{Output force}}{\text{Input force}}$$

12. In a machine that has a mechanical advantage of more than 1, the

___output___ force is greater than the ___input___ force.

▶ Efficiency of Machines (pages 106–107)

13. In any machine, some work is wasted overcoming ___friction___ .

14. The comparison of a machine's output work to its input work is

___efficiency___ .

15. What is the formula you use to calculate the efficiency of a machine?

$$\text{Efficiency} = \frac{\text{Output work}}{\text{Input work}} \times 100\%$$

© Prentice-Hall, Inc.

16. The mechanical advantage that a machine provides in a real situation is called the _____actual_____ mechanical advantage.

17. The mechanical advantage of a machine without friction is called the machine's _____ideal_____ mechanical advantage.

📖 Reading Skill Practice

By looking carefully at photographs and illustrations in textbooks, you can help yourself understand what you have read. Look carefully at Figure 5 on page 103. What important idea does this illustration communicate?

A machine can make a task easier in three ways. It can multiply the input force. It can multiply the distance over which the force is exerted. Or it can neither multiply force or distance; in that case, a machine changes the direction in which you exert your force.

· ·

SECTION 4-3 **Simple Machines** (pages 110-120)

This section describes the six kinds of simple machines. It also explains how to calculate the advantage of using simple machines.

▶ Introduction (page 110)

1. What are the six basic kinds of simple machines?

a. _____inclined plane_____ b. _____wedge_____ c. _____screw_____

d. _____lever_____ e. _____wheel and axle_____ f. _____pulley_____

▶ Inclined Plane (pages 111–112)

2. What is an inclined plane? _____An inclined plane is a flat, slanted surface._____

_____

3. What formula do you use to determine the ideal mechanical advantage of an inclined plane?

$$\text{Ideal mechanical advantage} = \frac{\text{Length of incline}}{\text{Height of incline}}$$

CHAPTER 4, Work and Machines (continued)

4. Circle the letter of each sentence that is true about inclined planes.

   (a.) The necessary input force is less than the output force.

   (b.) A ramp is an example of an inclined plane.

   c. The necessary input force is more than the output force.

   (d.) An inclined plane allows you to exert your force over a longer distance.

5. You can increase the _____efficiency_____ of an inclined plane by decreasing the friction.

▶ Wedge (page 112)

6. What is a wedge? __A wedge is a device that is thick at one end and tapers__ __to a thin edge at the other end.__

   _____

7. Is the following sentence true or false? In a wedge, the inclined plane itself moves. _____true_____

8. Is the following sentence true or false? A wedge multiples force to do the job. _____true_____

▶ Screws (page 113)

9. What is a screw? __A screw is an inclined plane wrapped around a cylinder.__

   _____

10. A spiral inclined plane forms the _____threads_____ of a screw.

11. When using a screwdriver to twist a screw into a piece of wood, where is the input force applied and where is the output force exerted?

    The input force is applied to the handle of the screwdriver, which exerts a

    force on the threads of the screw. As the screw turns, the threads exert an

    output force on the wood.

© Prentice-Hall, Inc.

▶ Levers (pages 113–115)

12. What is a lever? A lever is a rigid bar that is free to pivot, or rotate, around

a fixed point.

_____

13. The fixed point that a lever pivots around is called the _____fulcrum_____.

14. Circle the letter of each sentence that is true about levers.

   (a.) A lever increases the effect of your input force.

   (b.) There are three different types of levers.

   (c.) A lever changes the direction of your input force.

   d. The fulcrum is always located at the same place on a lever.

15. On each diagram below, draw a triangle below the lever to show where the fulcrum is located on each class of lever.

First-class levers   **Second-class levers**   **Third-class levers**

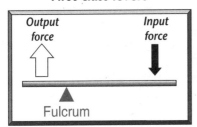
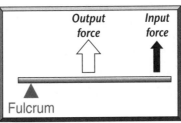

16. Complete the following table about levers.

Levers	
Class of Lever	**Examples**
Second-class lever	Door, wheel barrow, bottle opener
First-class lever	Seesaw, scissors, pliers
Third-class lever	Baseball bat, shovel, rake

17. What formula do you use to calculate the ideal mechanical advantage of a lever?

$$\text{Ideal mechanical advantage} = \frac{\text{Distance from fulcrum to input force}}{\text{Distance from fulcrum to output force}}$$

CHAPTER 4, Work and Machines (continued)

▶ Wheel and Axle (pages 116–118)

18. What is a wheel and axle? __A wheel and axle is a simple machine made of__

__two circular or cylindrical objects that are fastened together and that rotate__

__around a common axis.__

19. What formula do you use to calculate the ideal mechanical advantage
of a wheel and axle?

Ideal mechanical advantage = $\dfrac{\text{Radius of wheel}}{\text{radius of axle}}$

▶ Pulley (pages 118–119)

20. What is a pulley? __A pulley is a grooved wheel with a rope (or chain, or__

__even a steel cable) wrapped around it.__

21. What kind of pulley changes the direction of the input force but does

not change the amount of force you apply? __fixed pulley__

22. What kind of pulley has an ideal mechanical advantage of 2?

____moveable pulley____

▶ Compound Machines (page 120)

23. What is a compound machine? __A compound machine is a machine that__

__utilizes two or more simple machines.__

24. What do you need to know to calculate the mechanical advantage of a

compound machine? __You must know the mechanical advantage of each__

__simple machine utilized in the compound machine.__

25. A system of ____gears____ is a device with toothed wheels that
fit into one another.

© Prentice-Hall, Inc.

SECTION 4-4 Machines in the Human Body
(pages 124-126)

This section describes how the body uses natural levers and wedges.

▶ **Living Levers** (pages 124–126)

1. What do most of the levers in your body consist of? _They consist of_

   bones and muscles.

2. Your muscles are attached to your bones by tough connective tissue

   called _____tendons_____.

3. In a living lever in your body, what acts as the lever's fulcrum?

   The joint near where the tendon is attached to the bone acts as the fulcrum.

4. On the illustration of a living lever, label each arrow to show where the
   input force and the output force are located. Also show where the
   fulcrum is located.

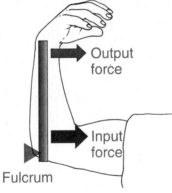

Output force

Input force

Fulcrum

▶ **Working Wedges** (page 126)

5. What simple machines do your incisors resemble? _____wedges_____

6. Explain how your front teeth are like an ax. _When you bite down on_

   something, the wedge shape of your teeth produces enough force to break

   it in half, just as an ax is used to split a log.

CHAPTER 4, Work and Machines *(continued)*

WordWise

Complete the sentences by using one of the scrambled words below.

Word Bank

lelyup   xela   oounmpdc   fiienycef   ttuuop   veelr

euojl   deegw   tupni   rwko   wecrs   clruumf   iclndeni   enihcam

A device that is thick at one end and tapers to a thin edge at the other end is a(n)
_____wedge_____.

A machine that utilizes two or more simple machines is called a(n) _____compound_____ machine.

The force exerted by a machine is called the _____output_____ force.

The fixed point that a lever pivots around is called the _____fulcrum_____.

You do _____work_____ on an object when you exert a force on the object that causes the object to move some distance.

A wheel and _____axle_____ is a simple machine made of two circular or cylindrical objects that are fastened together and that rotate around a common axis.

The _____efficiency_____ of a machine compares the output work to the input work.

A rigid bar that is free to pivot, or rotate, about a fixed point is a(n) _____lever_____.

The force you exert on a machine is called the _____input_____ force.

A(n) _____inclined_____ plane is a flat, slanted surface.

A grooved wheel with a rope wrapped around it is a(n) _____pulley_____.

A device with which you can do work in a way that is easier or more effective is a(n)
_____machine_____.

The SI unit of work is called the _____joule_____.

A(n) _____screw_____ can be thought of as an inclined plane wrapped around a cylinder.

Science Explorer *Focus on Physical Science*

MathWise

For the problems below, show your calculations. If you need more space, use another sheet of paper. Write the answers for the problems on the lines below.

▶ Calculating Work (pages 100–101)

1. Work = 10 N × 35 m = _____350 J_____

2. An elevator lifts a man with a weight of 500 N up three floors, or 30 m. How much work did the elevator do?

   Work = 500 N × 30 m = 15,000 J

   Answer: _____Work = 15,000 J_____

▶ Mechanical Advantage (page 105)

3. Mechanical advantage = $\dfrac{60 \text{ N}}{15 \text{ N}}$ = _____4_____

4. Suppose you exert of force of 2,800 N to lift a desk up onto a porch. But if you use a ramp, you need to exert a force of only 1,400 N to push it up the ramp onto the porch. What is the mechanical advantage of the ramp?

   Mechanical advantage = $\dfrac{2,800 \text{ N}}{1,400 \text{ N}}$ = 2

   Answer: _____Mechanical advantage = 2_____

▶ Calculating Efficiency (pages 106–107)

5. Efficiency = $\dfrac{100 \text{ J}}{200 \text{ J}}$ × 100% = _____50%_____

6. You do 4,000 J of work using a sledge hammer. The sledge hammer does 3,000 J of work on the spike. What is the efficiency of the sledge hammer?

   Efficiency = $\dfrac{3,000 \text{ J}}{4,000 \text{ J}}$ × 100% = 0.75 × 100% = 75%

   Answer: _____Efficiency = 75%_____

CHAPTER 4, Work and Machines (continued)

▶ Advantage of an Inclined Plane (page 111)

7. Ideal mechanical advantage = $\dfrac{8 \text{ m}}{2 \text{ m}}$ = _____ 4 _____

8. Suppose you built a ramp to the front door of the post office for people using wheel chairs. The post office door is 3 m above the level of the sidewalk. The ramp you build is 15 m long. What is the ideal mechanical advantage of your ramp?

Ideal mechanical advantage = $\dfrac{15 \text{ m}}{3 \text{ m}}$ = 5

Answer: _____ Ideal mechanical advantage = 5 _____

▶ Advantage of a Lever (page 114)

9. Ideal mechanical advantage = $\dfrac{4 \text{ m}}{2 \text{ m}}$ = _____ 2 _____

10. Suppose you held the handles of a wheel barrow 2.4 m from where they are attached to the wheel. The heavy stone in the wheel barrow was 1.2 m from the wheel. What is the ideal mechanical advantage of the wheel barrow?

Ideal mechanical advantage = $\dfrac{2.4 \text{ m}}{1.2 \text{ m}}$ = 2

Answer: _____ Ideal mechanical advantage = 2 _____

▶ Advantage of a Wheel and Axle (pages 117–118)

11. Ideal mechanical advantage = $\dfrac{36 \text{ cm}}{3 \text{ cm}}$ = _____ 12 _____

12. Suppose the radius of your bicycle's wheel is 30 cm. The radius of the bicycle's axle is just 5 cm. What is the ideal mechanical advantage of that wheel and axle?

Ideal mechanical advantage = $\dfrac{30 \text{ cm}}{5 \text{ cm}}$ = 6

Answer: _____ Ideal mechanical advantage = 6 _____

CHAPTER 5

ENERGY AND POWER

• •

SECTION 5–1 **The Nature of Energy**
(pages 132-137)

This section explains how work and energy are related. It also identifies the two basic kinds of energy and describes some different forms of energy.

▶ What Is Energy? (pages 132–133)

1. The ability to do work or cause change is called _____energy_____.

2. Why can work be thought of as the transfer of energy? ___When an object___ or organism does work on an object, some of the energy is transferred to the object.

▶ Kinetic Energy (pages 133–134)

3. What are the two general kinds of energy?

   a. ___kinetic energy___   b. ___potential energy___

4. What is kinetic energy? ___The energy of motion___

5. The kinetic energy of an object depends on both its ___mass___ and its ___velocity___.

6. Kinetic energy increases as velocity ___increases___.

7. What formula do you use to calculate kinetic energy?

   $$\text{Kinetic energy} = \frac{\text{Mass} \times \text{Velocity}^2}{2}$$

8. Because velocity is squared in the kinetic energy equation, doubling an object's velocity will ___quadruple___ its kinetic energy.

CHAPTER 5, Energy and Power (continued)

▶ Potential Energy (pages 134–135)

9. What is potential energy? __Potential energy is energy that is stored and__ __held in readiness.__

10. What is the potential energy called that is associated with objects that can be stretched or compressed? __elastic potential energy__

11. What is potential energy called that depends on height? __gravitational__ __potential energy__

12. What is the formula you use to determine the gravitational potential energy of an object? __Gravitational potential energy = Weight × Height__

13. Is the following sentence true or false? The greater the height of an object, the greater its gravitational potential energy. __true__

▶ Different Forms of Energy (pages 136–137)

14. What is mechanical energy? __Mechanical energy is the energy associated__ __with the motion or position of an object.__

15. What is thermal energy? __Thermal energy is the total energy of the__ __particles in an object.__

_____

16. Is the following sentence true or false? When the thermal energy of an object increases, its particles move faster. __true__

17. The potential energy stored in chemical bonds that hold chemical compounds together is called __chemical energy__.

18. What kind of energy is stored in the foods you eat? __chemical energy__

19. The energy that moving electric charges carry is called __electrical__ energy.

20. What kind of energy is stored in the nucleus of an atom?

_____ nuclear energy _____

21. Complete the table below on the different forms of energy.

Different Forms of Energy	
Form of Energy	**Examples**
Mechanical energy	School bus moving, frog leaping, sounds being made
Thermal energy	Ice cream melting, object feeling warm
Chemical energy	Foods, matches, stored in body cells
Electrical energy	Static shock, batteries, power lines
Electromagnetic energy	Visible light, ultraviolet radiation, microwaves, infrared radiation
Nuclear energy	Nuclear fission, nuclear fusion

 Reading Skill Practice

Outlining is a way to help yourself understand and remember what you have read. Write an outline of Section 5–1, The Nature of Energy. In your outline, copy the headings in the textbook. Under each heading, write the main idea of that part of the section. Then list the details that support, or back up, the main idea.

The major heads of student's outlines of the section should be *What Is Energy?, Kinetic Energy, Potential Energy,* and *Different Forms of Energy.* The section's subheads should form the next level of the outline.

SECTION 5-2 **Energy Conversion and Conservation** (pages 140-145)

This section explains how different forms of energy are related and describes the law of conservation of energy.

▶ **Conversions Between Forms of Energy** (page 141)

1. A change from one form of energy to another is called a(n)

_____ energy conversion _____.

CHAPTER 5, Energy and Power *(continued)*

2. Is the following sentence true or false? Most forms of energy can be converted into other forms. _____true_____

3. Describe the conversion of chemical energy to mechanical energy in your body. __The body converts the chemical energy in food to the__ mechanical energy needed to move muscles. _____

_____

▶ Kinetic and Potential Energy (pages 142–143)

4. When you throw an orange up into the air, what kind of energy increases as its height increases? ___potential energy___

5. As an orange falls from its greatest height, what kind of energy increases and what kind of energy decreases? __Its kinetic energy__ increases, and its potential energy decreases. _____

_____

6. On the diagram of a moving pendulum, label the places where the pendulum has maximum potential energy and where it has maximum kinetic energy.

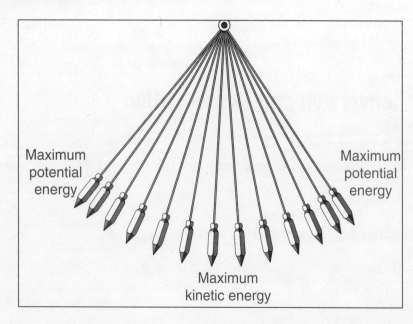

Maximum potential energy

Maximum potential energy

Maximum kinetic energy

© Prentice-Hall, Inc.

▶ Conservation of Energy (pages 144–145)

7. What does the law of conservation of energy state? _When one form of_

energy is converted to another, no energy is destroyed in the process.

_____

8. Friction converts mechanical energy to _____thermal_____ energy.

9. Circle the letter of the sentence that explains why no machine is 100 percent efficient.

   a. Electrical energy is converted to mechanical energy by fuel.

   (b.) Mechanical energy is converted to thermal energy by friction.

   c. Thermal energy is converted to mechanical energy by friction.

   d. Mechanical energy is converted to electrical energy by a spark.

10. How did Albert Einstein's theory of relativity change the law of

conservation of energy? _He explained that energy can sometimes be_

created by destroying matter.

_____

_____

11. Is the following sentence true or false? Matter and energy can be

converted back and forth. _____true_____

▶ Conserving Energy (page 145)

12. Compare and contrast the meanings of *conserving energy* in the table.

	Conserving Energy
In Environmental Science	Conserving energy means to save energy, or not waste it.
In Physical Science	Conserving energy means that the quantity of energy remains constant. Energy is always conserved because its total quantity does not change.

CHAPTER 5, Energy and Power *(continued)*

. . . .

SECTION 5–3 Energy Conversions and Fossil Fuels
(pages 146-149)

This section explains the source of the energy stored in fossil fuels and describes how energy is converted when fossil fuels are used.

▶ **Formation of Fossil Fuels (pages 147–149)**

1. Is the following sentence true or false? A fuel is a material that stores chemical potential energy. _____true_____

2. Circle the letters of the following that are fossil fuels.

   (a.)coal **b.** sunlight (c.)petroleum (d.)natural gas

3. Where did the energy in fossil fuels originally come from?
   _____the sun_____

4. What energy conversion takes place on the sun? __During nuclear fusion,__
   nuclear energy is converted to electromagnetic energy. _____

   _____

5. What energy conversion takes place during photosynthesis?
   Electromagnetic energy from the sun is converted to chemical potential energy. __

   _____

▶ **Use of Fossil Fuels (page 149)**

6. How is the potential chemical energy of fossil fuels released?
   It is released by burning the fossil fuels. _____

7. The process of burning fossil fuels is known as _____combustion_____.

8. What energy conversion occurs during combustion? __The fuel's__
   chemical potential energy is converted to thermal energy. _____

   _____

9. In a modern coal-fired power plant, the mechanical energy of turbines is converted into electrical energy by ___generators___.

....

Power
(pages 150-154)

This section describes how you calculate power and explains the difference between power and energy.

▶ **What Is Power?** (pages 150–151)

1. What is power? __Power is the rate at which work is done or the amount of__ __work done in a unit of time.__

_____

2. Is the following sentence true or false? You exert more power when you run up a flight of stairs than when you walk up the stairs.

___true___

3. Circle the letter of each sentence that is true about a device that is twice as powerful as another device.

   a. The more powerful device can do half the amount of work in half the time.

   (**b.**)The more powerful device can do the same amount of work in half the time.

   (**c.**)The more powerful device can do twice the amount of work in the same amount of time.

   d. The more powerful device can do twice the amount of work in twice the amount of time.

4. What is the formula you use to calculate power?

$$\text{Power} = \frac{\text{Work}}{\text{Time}}$$

5. Rewrite the equation for power in a way that shows what work equals.

$$\text{Power} = \frac{\text{Force} \times \text{Distance}}{\text{Time}}$$

CHAPTER 5, Energy and Power *(continued)*

6. 1 J/s = 1 _____watt_____

7. Is the following sentence true or false? Power is often measured in

larger units than watts. _____true_____

8. 1 kilowatt = _____1,000_____ watts

9. Is the following sentence true or false? An electric power plant produces

millions of kilowatts. _____true_____

▶ Power and Energy (pages 152–153)

10. Is the following sentence true or false? Power is limited to situations in

which objects are moved. _____false_____

11. Power is the _____rate_____ at which energy is transferred from
one object to another or converted from one form to another.

12. The power of a light bulb is the rate at which _____electrical_____

energy is converted into _____electromagnetic_____ energy and

_____thermal_____ energy.

13. Why is a 100-watt light bulb brighter than a 40-watt light bulb?

The 100-watt light bulb gives off more energy per second than the 40-watt

light bulb.

_____

▶ Horsepower (page 154)

14. Circle the letter of each sentence that is true about the unit known as
horsepower.

a. Horsepower is an SI unit of power.

b. James Watt used the word *horsepower* to compare the work of a
steam engine with the work of a horse.

c. People use the unit horsepower when talking about automobile engines.

d. 1 horsepower = 746 watts

WordWise

Complete the following paragraphs using the list of words and phrases below. Each word or phrase is used only once.

Word Bank

law of conservation of energy   nuclear energy   kinetic energy   thermal energy
fossil fuels   electromagnetic energy   energy conversion   electrical energy
power   energy   mechanical energy   potential energy   chemical energy

In nature, things are constantly changing, and the identification of what causes changes is important in physical science. The ability to do work or cause change is called _____energy_____. There are two general kinds of energy. The energy of motion is called _____kinetic energy_____. Energy that is stored and held in readiness is called _____potential energy_____.

There are different forms of the two general kinds of energy. The energy associated with the motion or position of an object is called _____mechanical energy_____. The total energy of the particles of an object is called _____thermal energy_____. The potential energy stored in chemical bonds that hold chemical compounds together is called _____chemical energy_____. The energy that moving electric charges carry is called _____electrical energy_____. Visible light and other waves of energy are forms of _____electromagnetic energy_____. The energy stored in the nucleus of an atom is _____nuclear energy_____.

Most forms of energy can be converted into other forms. A change from one form of energy to another is called _____energy conversion_____. Such changes from one form of energy to another do not mean any energy is lost. The _____law of conservation of energy_____ states that when one form of energy is converted to another, no energy is destroyed in the process.

A fuel is a material that stores chemical potential energy. For many purposes, we use _____fossil fuels_____, such as coal, petroleum, and natural gas. The energy conversions in modern coal-fired power plants result in the electricity you use for home electrical devices. You use these devices to do work. The rate at which work is done, or the amount of work done in a unit of time, is called _____power_____.

CHAPTER 5, Energy and Power *(continued)*

MathWise

For the problems below, show your calculations. If you need more space, use another sheet of paper. Write the answers for the problems on the lines below.

▶ Calculating Gravitational Potential Energy (page 135)

1. Gravitational potential energy = 25 N × 10 m = _____250 J_____

2. A student stands at the edge of a diving board that is 3 m high. The student's weight is 350 N. What is the student's gravitational potential energy?

Gravitational potential energy = 350 N × 3 m = 1,050 J

Answer: ___Gravitational potential energy = 1,050 J___

3. Gravitational potential energy = 60 kg × 9.8 m/s² × 5 m = ___2,940 J___

4. Suppose a boulder has a mass of 25 kg, and it is perched on the edge of a cliff that is 45 m high. What is the gravitational potential energy of the boulder?

Gravitational potential energy = 25 kg × 9.8 m/s² × 45 m = 11,025 J

Answer: ___Gravitational potential energy = 11,025 J___

▶ Calculating Power (pages 150–151)

5. Power = $\dfrac{5{,}000 \text{ N} \times 15 \text{ m}}{3 \text{ s}}$ = ___25,000 W or 25 kW___

6. You exert a force of 300 N to lift a box 2 m from the floor to a shelf in 3 s. How much power did you use?

Power = $\dfrac{300 \text{ N} \times 2 \text{ m}}{3 \text{ s}}$ = 200 W

Answer: ___Power = 200 W___

© Prentice-Hall, Inc.

Science Explorer *Focus on Physical Science*

CHAPTER 6

THERMAL ENERGY AND HEAT

SECTION 6-1 **Temperature and Thermal Energy** (pages 160–162)

This section describes the three common temperature scales and explains how temperature differs from thermal energy.

▶ Temperature (pages 160–161)

1. Is the following sentence true or false? All particles of matter have kinetic energy. _____true_____

2. What is temperature? __Temperature is a measure of the average kinetic__ __energy of the individual particles of an object.__

_____

3. Which particles are moving faster, the particles of a mug of hot cocoa or the particles of a glass of cold chocolate milk? __The particles of a mug of__ __hot cocoa are moving faster.__

_____

▶ Temperature Scales (pages 161–162)

4. What are the three common scales for measuring temperature?

   a. __Fahrenheit scale__   b. __Celsius scale__   c. __Kelvin scale__

5. The most common temperature scale in the United States is the __Fahrenheit__ scale.

6. The temperature scale used in most of the world is the __Celsius__ scale.

CHAPTER 6, Thermal Energy and Heat *(continued)*

7. The temperature scale commonly used in physical science is the
   _____Kelvin_____ scale.

8. What are the intervals on the Fahrenheit scale called?
   _____degrees Fahrenheit_____

9. Which scale is divided into 100 equal parts between the freezing and
   boiling of water? _____Celsius scale_____

10. What is the temperature called at which no more energy can be
    removed from matter? _____absolute zero_____

11. Complete the following table. See Figure 2 on page 161.

Temperature Scales			
Scale	**Absolute zero**	**Water freezes**	**Water boils**
Fahrenheit	−460°	32°	212°
Celsius	−273°	0°	100°
Kelvin	0	273	373

▶ Thermal Energy (page 162)

12. The total energy of the particles in a substance is called
    _____thermal_____ energy.

13. Circle the letter of each sentence that is true of thermal energy.

    (a.)Thermal energy partly depends on the temperature of a substance.

    b. Thermal energy partly depends on the scale used to measure the
    temperature of a substance.

    (c.)Thermal energy partly depends on how the particles of a substance
    are arranged.

    (d.)Thermal energy partly depends on the number of particles of a
    substance.

SECTION 6-2 The Nature of Heat (pages 163-169)

This section explains how heat is related to thermal energy and describes three ways heat is transferred.

▶ Introduction (pages 163–164)

1. What is heat? <u>Heat is the movement of thermal energy from a substance</u>

   <u>at a higher temperature to another at a lower temperature.</u>

   _____

   _____

2. Is the following sentence true or false? Heat is thermal energy moving

   from a warmer object to a cooler object. _____<u>true</u>_____

▶ How Is Heat Transferred? (pages 164–166)

3. Circle the letter of the three ways that heat can move.

   (a.) conduction   **b.** current   (c.) radiation   (d.) convection

4. Think of a metal spoon in a pot of hot water. How do the particles of

   the water affect the particles of the spoon? <u>The fast-moving particles of</u>

   <u>the hot water collide with the particles of the spoon, causing the particles of</u>

   <u>the spoon to move faster. As the particles move faster, the metal spoon</u>

   <u>becomes hotter.</u>

   _____

5. How is heat transferred in convection? <u>Heat is transferred by the</u>

   <u>movement of currents within a fluid.</u>

   _____

6. The circular motion of fluid caused by rising and sinking of heated and

   cooler fluid is known as a(n) _____<u>convection current</u>_____.

CHAPTER 6, Thermal Energy and Heat *(continued)*

7. The illustration shows a pot of liquid on a stovetop burner. Draw the convection currents that result.

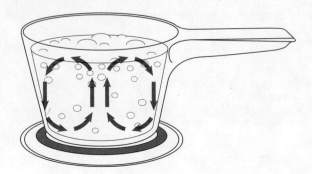

8. Is the following sentence true or false? Radiation requires matter to transfer energy. _____false_____

9. Complete the table.

Heat Transfer		
Process	**How Heat Moves**	**Example**
Conduction	Transferred from one particle of matter to another without the movement of matter itself	Metal spoon in hot water
Convection	Transferred by the movement of currents within a fluid	Pot of hot water on a stove, heating a building or the atmosphere
Radiation	Transferred by electromagnetic waves	Bonfire, heat lamp, the sun heating Earth

▶ Heat Moves One Way (page 166)

10. When heat flows from one substance to another, what happens to the temperature of the substance giving off the heat and to the temperature of the substance receiving the heat? The temperature of the substance giving off the heat decreases, while the temperature of the substance receiving the heat increases.

© Prentice-Hall, Inc.

11. Why can't ice transfer coldness into another substance? <u>There is no</u>

<u>such thing as "coldness."</u>

_____

▶ Conductors and Insulators (pages 167–168)

12. A material that conducts heat well is called a(n) <u>conductor</u>.

13. A material that does not conduct heat well is called a(n)

<u>insulator</u>.

14. Classify each of the following materials as either a conductor or an insulator by writing the correct term on the line.

a. air <u>insulator</u>   **b.** wool <u>insulator</u>

c. wood <u>insulator</u>   **d.** tile <u>conductor</u>

e. silver <u>conductor</u>   **f.** fiberglass <u>insulator</u>

▶ Specific Heat (pages 168–169)

15. What is a substance's specific heat? <u>It is the amount of energy required</u>

<u>to raise the temperature of 1 kilogram of the substance by 1 kelvin.</u>

_____

16. What is the unit of measure for specific heat? <u>joules per kilogram-</u>

<u>kelvin, or J/(kg • K)</u>

17. Materials with a high specific heat can absorb a great deal of thermal

energy without a great change in <u>temperature</u>.

18. The energy gained or lost by an object is related to which of the following? Circle the letter of the terms that answer the question.

(**a.**)mass   **b.** volume   (**c.**)specific heat   (**d.**)temperature

19. What is the formula you can use to calculate thermal energy changes?

Change in energy = Mass × Specific heat × Change in temperature

_____

CHAPTER 6, Thermal Energy and Heat *(continued)*

SECTION 6-3 **Thermal Energy and States of Matter** (pages 173-178)

This section explains what causes matter to change state. It also explains why matter expands when it is heated.

▶ Three States of Matter (page 174)

1. Is the following sentence true or false? All matter can exist in three states.
   _____true_____

2. Circle the letter of the terms that identify states of matter.
   a. water   (**b.**)gas   (**c.**)liquid   (**d.**)solid

3. The particles that make up a(n) _____solid_____ are packed together in a relatively fixed position.

4. Circle the letter of each statement that is true about liquids.
   (**a.**)Liquids have a definite volume.
   b. Liquids have a fixed shape.
   (**c.**)Liquid particles can move around.
   d. Liquid particles are moving around so fast that they don't even stay close together.

5. In which state of matter can the particles only vibrate back and forth?
   _____solid_____

6. In which state of matter do the particles expand to fill all the space available? _____gas_____

▶ Changes of State (pages 174-175)

7. What is a change of state? ___It is the physical change from one state of___
   ___matter to another.___
   _____

8. Circle the letter of each sentence that is true.

   (a.) The particles of a gas move faster than the particles of a liquid.

   b. The particles of a solid move faster than the particles of a gas.

   (c.) The particles of a liquid move faster than the particles of a solid.

   (d.) The particles of a gas move faster than the particles of a solid.

9. Matter will change from one state to another if _____thermal energy_____ is absorbed or released.

10. On the graph below, write labels for the regions of the graph that represent the gas, liquid, and solid states of matter.

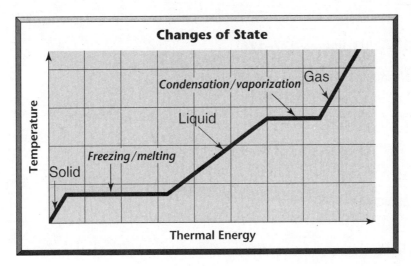

▶ Solid-Liquid Changes of State (pages 175–176)

11. The change in state from a solid to a liquid is called _____melting_____.

12. The temperature at which a solid changes to a liquid is called the _____melting point_____.

13. The change in state from a liquid to a solid is called _____freezing_____.

14. The temperature at which a substance changes from a liquid to a solid is called its _____freezing point_____.

▶ Liquid-Gas Changes of State (pages 176–177)

15. What is vaporization? _____Vaporization is the process by which matter changes from the liquid to the gas state._____

CHAPTER 6, Thermal Energy and Heat *(continued)*

16. If vaporization takes place on the surface of a liquid it is called
_____evaporation_____.

17. What is vaporization called when it occurs below the surface of a
liquid? _____boiling_____

18. The temperature at which liquid boils is called its _____boiling point_____.

19. A change from the gas state to the liquid state is called
_____condensation_____.

▶ Thermal Expansion (pages 177–178)

20. The expanding of matter when it is heated is known as
_____thermal expansion_____.

21. What happens to the liquid in a thermometer when it is heated?
It expands and climbs up the tube.

22. Heat-regulating devices are called _____thermostats_____.

23. In thermostats, what are strips of two different metals joined together
called? _____bimetallic strips_____

24. In thermostats, bimetallic strips are used because different metals
_____expand_____ at different rates.

 Reading Skill Practice

You can often increase your understanding of what you've read by making comparisons. A compare/contrast table helps you do this. On a separate sheet of paper, draw a table to compare the three states of matter as explained on page 174. The three row heads will be *Solid, Liquid,* and *Gas.* Column heads should include *State, Particles, Shape,* and *Volume.* For more information about compare/contrast tables, see page 832 in the Skills Handbook of your textbook.

Student's tables should include the basic information about the three states contained in the short paragraphs on page 174.

Science Explorer *Focus on Physical Science*

SECTION 6-4 Uses of Heat (pages 179-182)

This section describes how thermal energy is related to heat engines and refrigerators.

▶ Heat Engines (pages 179–181)

1. To fire a steam locomotive, the thermal energy of a coal fire must be

   converted to the _____mechanical_____ energy of the moving train.

2. The conversion of thermal energy to mechanical energy requires a device

   called a(n) _____heat engine_____.

3. What is the process of burning a fuel, such as coal or gasoline?

   _____combustion_____

4. How are heat engines classified? ___They are classified according to whether___

   ___combustion takes place outside the engine or inside the engine.___

   _____

5. Complete the compare/contrast table.

Heat Engines		
Type	**Where Fuel Is Burned**	**Example**
External combustion engines	Outside the engine	Steam engine
Internal combustion engines	Inside the engine	Diesel and gasoline engines

6. In a steam engine, what does the steam move back and forth inside a

   cylinder? _____a piston_____

7. In an internal combustion engine, each up or down movement of a

   piston is called a(n) _____stroke_____.

8. When a spark ignites the mixture of gas and fuel in a four-stroke engine,

   stored chemical energy is converted to _____thermal_____ energy.

CHAPTER 6, Thermal Energy and Heat (continued)

9. Complete the flowchart below, which describes the process that occurs in each cylinder of a four-stroke engine.

> A mixture of fuel and air is drawn into the cylinder during the _____intake_____ stroke.

↓

> During the _____compression_____ stroke, the mixture is squeezed into a smaller space.

↓

> A spark plug ignites the mixture during _____ignition_____, heating up the gas.

↓

> During the _____power_____ stroke, the heated gas expands and pushes the piston down, which moves the crankshaft.

↓

> During the _____exhaust_____ stroke, the piston pushes the heated gas out, making room for new fuel and air.

▶ Refrigerators (page 182)

10. A refrigerator transfers thermal energy from a cool area to a(n) _____warm_____ area.

11. What provides the energy for a refrigerator to transfer energy from inside to outside? __An electric motor provides the energy.__

_____

12. Where does the gas that circulates through the tubes inside the refrigerator walls lose thermal energy? __It loses energy in the compressor__ motor.

WordWise

Use the clues below to identify key terms from Chapter 6. Write the terms on the lines, putting one letter in each blank. When you finish, the word enclosed in the diagonal will reveal an important term related to kinetic energy.

Clues

1. The expanding of matter when it is heated
2. Thermal energy that is transferred
3. Process of burning a fuel
4. Process by which matter changes from the liquid to the gas state
5. Heat is transferred by the movement of these currents.
6. Vaporization that takes place at the surface of a liquid
7. A material that does not conduct heat well
8. The change of state from solid to liquid
9. The temperature at which no more energy can be removed from matter
10. A material that conducts heat well
11. The physical change from one state of matter to another

1. t h e r m a l   e x p a n s i o n
2. h e a t
3. c o m b u s t i o n
4. v a p o r i z a t i o n
5. c o n v e c t i o n
6. e v a p o r a t i o n
7. i n s u l a t o r
8. m e l t i n g
9. a b s o l u t e   z e r o
10. c o n d u c t o r
11. c h a n g e   o f   s t a t e

CHAPTER 6, Thermal Energy and Heat *(continued)*

MathWise

For the problems below, show your calculations. If you need more space, use another sheet of paper. Write the answers for the problems on the lines below.

▶ **Specific Heat** (pages 168–169)

1. Heat absorbed = (2 kg)(450 J/(kg·K))(5 K) = _____ 4,500 J _____

2. Heat absorbed = (7 kg)(664 J/(kg·K))(20 K) = _____ 92,960 J _____

3. Aluminum has a specific heat of 903 J/(kg·K). How much heat is required to raise the temperature of 6 kilograms of aluminum 15 kelvins?

   Heat absorbed = (6 kg)(903 J/(kg·K))(15 K) = 81,270 J

   Answer: _____ Heat absorbed = 81,270 J _____

4. Sand has a specific heat of 670 J/(kg·K). How much heat is required to raise the temperature of 16 kilograms of sand 5 kelvins?

   Heat absorbed = (16 kg)(670 J/(kg·K))(5 K) = 53,600 J

   Answer: _____ Heat absorbed = 53,600 J _____

5. Water has a specific heat of 4,180 J/(kg·K). How much heat is required to raise the temperature of 3 kilograms of water 20 kelvins?

   Heat absorbed = (3 kg)(4,180 J/(kg·K))(20 K) = 250,800 J

   Answer: _____ Heat absorbed = 250,800 J _____

Science Explorer *Focus on Physical Science*

CHAPTER 7

CHARACTERISTICS OF WAVES

SECTION 7-1 **What Are Waves?** (pages 196-199)

This section explains what causes waves and identifies the three main types of waves.

▶ **Waves and Energy** (pages 196–197)

1. What is a wave? _A wave is a disturbance that transfers energy from place_

to place.

_____

2. The material through which a wave travels is called a(n) __medium__.

3. Circle the letter of each of the following that can act as mediums.

   a. solids ⃝   **b.** liquids ⃝   **c.** gases ⃝   **d.** empty space

4. Waves that require a medium through which to travel are called

   ___mechanical waves___.

5. Is the following sentence true or false? When waves travel through a

   medium, they carry the medium with them. ___false___

6. Explain what happens to a duck on the surface of a pond when a wave

   passes under it. _The duck moves up and down but does not move along_

   the surface of the water.

7. Give an example of a wave that can travel through empty space. _A light_

   wave from the sun can travel through empty space.

8. Waves are created when a source of energy causes a medium to

   ___vibrate___.

CHAPTER 7, Characteristics of Waves *(continued)*

9. What is a vibration? __A vibration is a repeated back-and-forth or up-and-__
down motion.

▶ **Types of Waves** (pages 198–199)

10. How are waves classified? __Waves are classified according to how they__
move.

11. Waves that move the medium at right angles to the direction in which
the waves are traveling are called __transverse waves__.

12. Suppose you move the free end of a rope up and down to create a wave.
In that case, the rope is the medium. What is the relationship between the
movement of the wave and the movement of the particles of the medium?
__As a transverse wave moves in one direction, the particles of the medium__
__move across the direction of the wave.__

13. The highest parts of a transverse wave are called __crests__.

14. The lowest parts of a transverse wave are called __troughs__.

15. What type of waves move the particles of the medium parallel to the
direction that the waves are traveling? __longitudinal waves__

16. In longitudinal waves in a spring, the parts where the coils are close
together are called __compressions__.

17. In longitudinal waves in a spring, the parts where the coils are spread
out are called __rarefactions__.

18. Waves that are combinations of transverse and longitudinal waves are
called __surface waves__.

19. Where do surface waves occur? __They occur at the surface between two__
mediums.

© Prentice-Hall, Inc.

20. In surface waves, the combination of motions produces
_____circular motion_____.

21. Complete this concept map about types of waves.

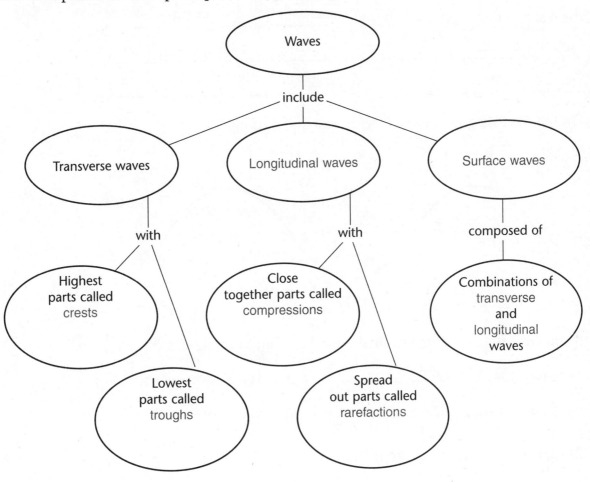

. . . .

SECTION 7-2 **Properties of Waves** (pages 200–205)

This section describes the basic properties of waves. It also explains how a wave's speed is related to its wavelength and frequency.

▶ **Introduction** (page 200)

1. What are the basic properties of waves?

a. ___amplitude___   b. ___wavelength___

c. ___frequency___   d. ___speed___

CHAPTER 7, Characteristics of Waves *(continued)*

▶ Wave Diagrams (pages 200–201)

2. On the transverse wave in Figure 5 on page 201, what does the line called the rest position represent? It represents the position of the rope before it is disturbed.

_____

3. On the wave diagram below, label a crest and a trough.

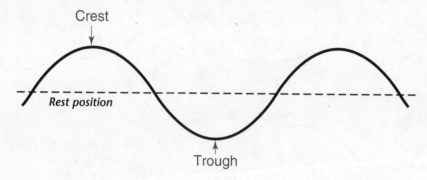

4. If you were to draw a longitudinal wave, you should think of the compressions as _____ crests _____ on a transverse wave and the rarefactions as _____ troughs _____ on a transverse wave.

▶ Amplitude (pages 201–202)

5. The maximum distance the particles of the medium carrying a wave move away from their rest position is called the wave's _____ amplitude _____.

6. Explain what the amplitude of a water wave is. It is the maximum distance a water particle moves above or below the surface level of calm water.

7. The amplitude of a wave is a direct measure of its _____ energy _____.

8. What is the amplitude of a longitudinal wave? It's a measure of how compressed or rarefied the medium becomes.

_____

9. Circle the letter of each phrase that correctly defines the amplitude of a transverse wave.

   a. The distance from the bottom of a trough to the top of a crest

   (b.)The maximum distance the particles of the medium move up or down from their rest position

   c. The maximum distance from one point on the rest position to another point on the rest position

   (d.)The distance from the rest position to a crest or to a trough

10. Suppose a longitudinal wave has crowded compressions and loose rarefactions. Does it have a large or a small amplitude?

    _____large_____

▶ Wavelength (page 203)

11. The distance between two corresponding parts of a wave is its

    _____wavelength_____ .

12. How can you find the wavelength of a longitudinal wave? ___You can___ measure the distance from one compression to the next. _____

▶ Frequency (page 204)

13. The number of complete waves that pass a given point in a certain amount of time is called the wave's ___frequency___ .

14. If you make a wave in a rope so that one wave passes every second, what is its frequency? ___1 wave per second_____

15. Circle the letter of the unit used to measure frequency.

    a. watt   **b.** seconds   **c.** joule   (d.)hertz

▶ Speed (pages 204–205)

16. The speed of a wave is how far the wave travels in one unit of

    _____time_____ .

CHAPTER 7, Characteristics of Waves *(continued)*

Complete the following formulas.

17. Speed = <u>Wavelength × Frequency</u>

18. Frequency = $\dfrac{Speed}{Wavelength}$

19. Wavelength = $\dfrac{Speed}{Frequency}$

20. Circle the letter of each sentence that is true about the speed of waves.

   a. All sound waves travel at the same speed.

   (b.) In a given medium and under the same conditions, the speed of a wave is constant.

   (c.) If the temperature and pressure of air changes, the speed of sound waves traveling through the air will change.

   (d.) Waves in different mediums travel at different speeds.

21. If you increase the frequency of a wave, the wavelength must

   _____decrease_____.

· ·

SECTION 7-3 Interactions of Waves
(pages 206-211)

This section describes how waves bend and how waves interact with each other.

▶ Reflection *(page 206)*

1. On the illustration below, write labels and draw arrows to show the location of the angle of incidence and the angle of reflection.

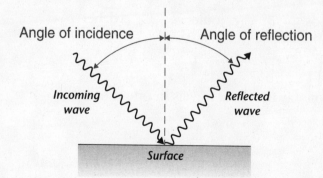

Angle of incidence   Angle of reflection

Incoming wave   Reflected wave

Surface

Science Explorer Focus on Physical Science

2. The bouncing back of a wave when it hits a surface through which it cannot pass is called _____reflection_____ .

3. What does the law of reflection state? __The angle of reflection equals the__ __angle of incidence.__

4. Is the following sentence true or false? Only transverse waves obey the law of reflection. _____false_____

▶ Refraction (page 207)

5. What happens when a wave moves from one medium into another medium at an angle? __It changes speed as it enters the second medium,__ __which causes it to bend.__

_____

6. The bending of waves as they enter a different medium is called _____refraction_____ .

7. All waves change speed when they enter a new medium, but they don't always bend. When does bending occur? __Bending occurs when one side__ __of the wave enters the new medium before the other side of the wave.__

_____

8. The bending of a wave entering a new medium occurs because the two sides of the wave are traveling at different _____speeds_____ .

▶ Diffraction (pages 207–208)

9. What happens when a wave passes a barrier or moves through a hole in a barrier? __It bends and spreads out.__

_____

10. The bending of waves around the edge of a barrier is known as _____diffraction_____ .

CHAPTER 7, Characteristics of Waves *(continued)*

11. Look at Figure 11 on page 208. What happens when waves go through a

hole in a barrier? __They spread out._____

▶ Interference (pages 208–209)

12. When two waves meet, they have an effect on each other. This

interaction is called ____interference_____.

13. When does constructive interference occur? __It occurs whenever two____

__waves combine to make a wave with a larger amplitude._____

_____

14. Describe what Figure 12A on page 209 shows. __The crests of the two____

__waves at the top align. The result is that the waves add together and____

__produce a wave with twice the original amplitude._____

_____

15. When the amplitudes of two waves combine with each other to

produce a smaller amplitude, the result is called __destructive_____

__interference_____.

16. In Figure 12B on page 209, why does the resulting wave at the bottom

have an amplitude of zero? __The crests of the first wave occur at the____

__same place as the troughs of the second wave, and they cancel each other____

__out._____

_____

17. What happens when two identical waves travel along the same path,

one a little behind the other? __The waves combine constructively in some____

__places and destructively in others._____

_____

▶ Standing Waves (pages 209–211)

18. What is a standing wave? A standing wave is a wave that appears to stand in one place, even though it is really two waves interfering as they pass through each other.

19. When destructive interference causes two waves to combine to produce an amplitude of zero, the point is called a(n) _____node_____.

20. The crests and troughs of a standing wave are called _____antinodes_____.

21. Is the following sentence true or false? Most objects have a natural frequency of vibration. _____true_____

22. When does resonance occur? It occurs when vibrations traveling through an object match the object's natural frequency.

23. Why are marching troops told to break step as they cross a bridge? If they all march across the bridge in perfect step, it is possible that the pounding could match the natural frequency of the bridge. The increased vibration could cause the bridge to collapse.

Match the interaction of water waves with its description.

Interaction	Description
b **24.** refraction	**a.** When two waves combine to make a wave with a smaller amplitude
e **25.** diffraction	**b.** When a wave bends as it moves from deep water to shallow water
c **26.** constructive interference	**c.** When two waves combine to make a wave with a larger amplitude
a **27.** destructive interference	**d.** When a wave bounces back from a barrier at the same angle it hits
d **28.** reflection	**e.** When waves bend or spread out around or behind an obstacle

CHAPTER 7, Characteristics of Waves *(continued)*

 Reading Skill Practice

You may sometimes forget the meanings of key terms that were introduced earlier in the textbook. When this happens, you can check the meanings of the terms in the Glossary, on pages 848–859, which gives meanings of all the key terms in the textbook. You'll find the terms in alphabetical order. Use the Glossary to review the meanings of all the key terms introduced in Section 7–3. Write their definitions on a separate sheet of paper.

The wording of the definitions in the Glossary are often slightly different than how the terms are defined in the flow of the text. Students should write the Glossary definition of each term.

SECTION 7-4 Seismic Waves
(pages 214–216)

This section explains how earthquakes produce waves that move through Earth.

▶ Types of Seismic Waves (page 215)

1. What movement creates stress on rock beneath Earth's surface? __The__ movement of Earth's plates creates stress on rock beneath Earth's surface. _____

_____

2. What happens when stress on rock builds up enough? __The rock breaks__ or changes shape, releasing energy in the form of waves or vibrations. _____

_____

3. The waves produced by earthquakes are known as _____ seismic waves _____.

4. Circle the letter of each sentence that is true about seismic waves.

   (a.) Seismic waves can travel from one side of Earth to the other.

   b. Even though seismic waves move through Earth, they don't carry energy.

   c. There is only one kind of seismic wave.

   (d.) Seismic waves ripple out in all directions from the point where the earthquake occurred.

Science Explorer *Focus on Physical Science*

© Prentice-Hall, Inc.

5. Why can't secondary waves travel through Earth's core? __Secondary__ waves cannot travel through liquid, and part of Earth's core is liquid.

_____

6. Which type of seismic waves arrives at distant points before any other seismic waves? __primary waves__

7. Which type of seismic waves produces the most severe ground movements? __surface waves__

8. Which type of seismic waves cannot be detected on the side of Earth opposite an earthquake? __secondary waves__

9. What are tsunamis? __Tsunamis are huge surface waves on the ocean__ caused by earthquakes that occur underwater.

_____

10. Complete the table about seismic waves.

Seismic Waves		
Type of Seismic Wave	**Transverse or Longitudinal?**	**Travel Characteristics**
Primary waves	Longitudinal	Travel through all parts of Earth
Secondary waves	Transverse	Travel through Earth but not through __core__
Surface waves	Combination	Travel only along Earth's __surface__

▶ **Detecting Seismic Waves** (page 216)

11. Circle the letter of the instrument scientists use to detect earthquakes.

   a. rarefactions   **b.** telegraphs   **c.** seismographs   **d.** tsunamis

12. What does a seismograph record? __It records the ground movements__ caused by seismic waves as they move through Earth.

_____

CHAPTER 7, Characteristics of Waves *(continued)*

13. What is the frame of a seismograph attached to? It is attached to the
ground.

14. What happens to a seismograph's frame when seismic waves arrive?
The frame shakes.

15. How can scientists tell how far away an earthquake was from a

seismograph? They can tell by measuring the time between the arrival of

P waves and S waves.

16. How can scientists tell where an earthquake occurred? They tell by

comparing readings from at least three seismographs at different places on

Earth.

17. Complete the flowchart about how geologists locate valuable substances
under Earth's surface.

To find out what is underground, geologists set off _____explosives_____.

↓

The explosives produce a small _____earthquake_____.

↓

The small earthquake sends out _____seismic waves_____.

↓

The seismic waves reflect from structures deep _____underground_____.

↓

The reflected seismic waves are recorded by _____seismographs_____
located around the site of the explosion.

WordWise

The block of letters below contains 16 key terms from Chapter 7. You might find them across, down, or on the diagonal. Use the clues to identify the terms you need to find. Circle each of the terms in the block of letters.

Clues

1. A disturbance that transfers energy from place to place
2. The ability to do work
3. The material through which a wave travels
4. A repeated back-and-forth or up-and-down motion
5. The highest part of a wave
6. The lowest part of a wave
7. The maximum distance the particles of the medium carrying the wave move away from their rest position
8. The distance between two corresponding parts of a wave
9. The number of complete waves that pass a given point in a certain amount of time
10. The unit in which frequency is measured
11. The bending of waves due to a change of speed
12. The bending of waves around the edge of a barrier
13. A point of zero amplitude on a standing wave
14. A point of maximum amplitude on a standing wave
15. What occurs when vibrations traveling through an object match the object's natural frequency
16. A huge surface wave on the ocean caused by an earthquake

```
d  t  s  u  n  a  m  i  p  a  q  w
i  v  i  b  r  a  t  i  o  n  m  a
f  r  e  q  u  e  n  c  y  t  a  v
f  u  n  n  p  w  b  v  x  i  m  e
r  e  f  r  a  c  t  i  o  n  p  l
a  x  e  n  e  r  g  y  u  o  l  e
c  i  w  a  v  e  z  a  p  d  i  n
t  z  e  v  s  z  u  j  e  t  g
i  o  d  d  e  t  x  w  e  g  u  t
o  o  u  t  r  o  u  g  h  y  d  h
n  i  r  e  s  o  n  a  n  c  e  r
n  y  h  m  e  d  i  u  m  r  t  z
```

CHAPTER 7, Characteristics of Waves *(continued)*

MathWise

For the problems below, show your calculations. If you need more space, use another sheet of paper. Write the answers for the problems on the lines below.

▶ Calculating Speed, Frequency, and Wavelength (pages 204–205)

1. Speed = 25 cm × 4 Hz = _____ 100 cm/s _____

2. A wave has a wavelength of 18 mm and a frequency of 3 Hz. At what speed does the wave travel?

Speed = 18 mm × 3 Hz = 54 mm/s

Answer: _____ Speed = 54 mm/s _____

3. Frequency = $\dfrac{75 \text{ cm/s}}{5 \text{ cm}}$ = _____ 15 Hz _____

4. The speed of a wave is 16 m/s and its wavelength is 4 m. What is its frequency?

Frequency = $\dfrac{16 \text{ m/s}}{4 \text{ m}}$ = 4 Hz

Answer: _____ Frequency = 4 Hz _____

5. Wavelength = $\dfrac{60 \text{ cm/s}}{3 \text{ Hz}}$ = _____ 20 cm _____

6. The speed of a wave on a violin is 125 m/s, and the frequency is 1,000 Hz. What is the wavelength of the wave?

Wavelength = $\dfrac{125 \text{ m/s}}{1{,}000 \text{ Hz}}$ = 0.125 m = 125 mm

Answer: _____ Wavelength = 125 mm _____

Science Explorer *Focus on Physical Science*

CHAPTER 8

SOUND

· ·

SECTION 8-1 **The Nature of Sound** (pages 222-226)

This section explains what sound is and identifies the factors that affect the speed of sound.

▶ **Sound and Longitudinal Waves** (pages 222–224)

1. What is sound? <u>Sound is a disturbance that travels through a medium as a</u> <u>longitudinal wave.</u>

2. Suppose a sound is made far away from you. When do you hear the sound? <u>You hear the sound when the disturbance reaches the air near your ears.</u> _____

3. Complete the flowchart about how you make sound with your voice.

You force air through the vocal cords of your <u>larynx</u> .

↓

The air rushing past your vocal cords makes them <u>vibrate</u> .

↓

The vibrating vocal cords produce longitudinal waves in the <u>air</u> .

↓

The longitudinal waves in the air travel to yours and others' <u>ears</u> .

CHAPTER 8, Sound *(continued)*

4. Why doesn't sound travel through outer space? <u>Sound can travel only if</u>

<u>there is a medium to transmit the compressions and rarefactions. In outer</u>

<u>space, there are no molecules to compress or rarefy.</u>

_____

5. What happens to sound waves when they go through a doorway into a

room? <u>Diffraction causes the sound waves to spread out throughout the</u>

<u>room.</u>

▶ The Speed of Sound (pages 224–225)

6. The speed of a sound depends on these three properties of the medium.

a. <u>elasticity</u> **b.** <u>density</u> **c.** <u>temperature</u>

7. Use the table in Figure 4 on page 224 to answer the following question. Through which medium does sound travel faster, air or water?

<u>air</u>

8. The ability of a material to bounce back after being disturbed is called

<u>elasticity</u>.

9. Is the following sentence true or false? Sound travels more slowly in

mediums that have a high degree of elasticity. <u>false</u>

10. How much matter, or mass, there is in a given amount of space, or

volume, is called <u>density</u>.

11. Is the following sentence true or false? In materials in the same state of

matter, sound travels slower in denser mediums. <u>true</u>

12. Why does sound travel slower through a medium when it is at a low

temperature? <u>At a low temperature, the particles of a medium are more</u>

<u>sluggish.</u>

▶ Moving Faster Than Sound (page 226)

13. In 1947, what did Captain Chuck Yeager do that nobody had ever done

before? ___He flew an airplane faster than the speed of sound.___

_____

14. In 1997, what did Andy Green do that nobody had ever done before?

He drove a land vehicle faster than the speed of sound.
_____

_____

. . . .

SECTION 8-2 Properties of Sound (pages 228-233)

This section describes several properties of sound, including loudness and pitch. It also explains what you hear as the source of a sound moves.

▶ Intensity and Loudness (pages 228–229)

1. The amount of energy a wave carries per second through a unit area is

called the sound wave's ____intensity____.

2. Describe the molecules of the medium when a sound wave carries a

large amount of energy. ___The molecules move a greater distance as the___

___sound waves pass by.___

3. What is loudness? ___Loudness describes what you actually hear.___

_____

4. In what units is loudness measured? ____decibels____

5. Each 10 dB increase in sound level represents how much of an increase

in intensity? ____tenfold____

6. Can loud music cause damage to your ears? ___It can cause damage after___

___long exposure.___

CHAPTER 8, Sound *(continued)*

▶ Frequency and Pitch (pages 230–231)

7. Circle the letter of each sentence that is true about how a person changes the pitch of sounds when singing.

   (a.) A person relaxes the vocal cords to produce lower-frequency sound waves.

   b. A person stretches the vocal cords to produce lower-frequency sound waves.

   (c.) A person stretches the vocal cords to produce higher-frequency sound waves.

   d. A person relaxes the vocal cords to produce higher-frequency sound waves.

8. Sound waves with frequencies above the normal human range of hearing are called _____ultrasound_____ .

9. Sound waves with frequencies below the normal human range of hearing are called _____infrasound_____ .

10. What is the pitch of a sound? The pitch of a sound is a description of how high or low the sound seems to a person.

11. What does the pitch of a sound you hear depend on? It depends on the frequency of the sound wave.

▶ The Doppler Effect (pages 232–233)

12. What is the Doppler effect? The Doppler effect is the apparent change in frequency as a wave source moves in relation to the listener.

13. Is the following sentence true or false? A sonic boom is a sound shock wave produced when the sound barrier is broken. _____true_____

14. Complete the table about the Doppler effect.

Doppler Effect		
Action	Change in Frequency—Higher or Lower?	Change in Pitch—Higher or Lower?
A police car with siren on moves toward you	Higher	Higher
A train with a band playing moves away from you	Lower	Lower
A train with a band playing moves toward you	Higher	Higher
A police car with siren on moves away from you	Lower	Lower

• •

SECTION 8-3 ## Combining Sound Waves
(pages 234-241)

This section explains what produces the quality of sounds. It also explains the difference between music and noise and describes what happens when sound waves interact.

▶ Sound Quality (page 235)

1. The resonant frequency of an object produces a pitch called the
_____fundamental tone_____.

2. When a string vibrates at several frequencies at the same time, the

higher frequencies produce sounds called _____overtones_____.

3. What describes the quality of the sound you hear? _____timbre_____

4. What makes up the timbre of a particular sound? _The blending of the_
fundamental tone and the overtones makes up the timbre.

_____

▶ Making Music (pages 236–239)

5. What is music? _Music is a set of tones combined in ways that are_

pleasing to the ear.

_____

CHAPTER 8, Sound *(continued)*

6. How do musicians vary the pitch on stringed instruments? _They place_

their fingers on different places along the string.

_____

7. Why do many stringed instruments have a box? _The box improves the_

quality of the sound produced by the strings.

_____

8. What vibrates within a brass instrument that the player can adjust?

The air column vibrates, and the musician can adjust it by pressing valves

or moving slides.

9. What vibrates when a player blows into the mouthpiece of a woodwind

instrument? _The reed vibrates, along with the column of air._

_____

10. Is the following sentence true or false? The sound a percussion
instrument makes depends on the material from which it is made.

_____true_____

11. Complete the table by classifying each instrument into one of the major
groups of instruments—Strings, Brass, Woodwinds, or Percussion.

Musical Instruments			
Instrument	**Major Group**	**Instrument**	**Major Group**
Guitar	Strings	Cello	Strings
Drums	Percussion	Oboe	Woodwinds
Violin	Strings	Trumpet	Brass
Trombone	Brass	Double bass	Strings
Clarinet	Woodwinds	Harp	Strings

© Prentice-Hall, Inc.

▶ Noise (page 237)

12. A mixture of sound waves that do not sound pleasing together is called
_____noise_____.

13. Circle the letter of each sentence that is true about noise.

(**a.**)Sounds that are music to some people are noise to others.

(**b.**)Noise has no pleasing timbre.

c. Sounds that have rhythm are always called noise.

(**d.**)Noise has no identifiable pitch.

14. The sound produced when notes that have no musical relationship are

played together is called _____dissonance_____.

▶ Interference of Sound Waves (pages 240–241)

15. When does interference of sound waves occur? ___It occurs when two or___

more sound waves interact.
_____

16. Is the following sentence true or false? When the interference of two
sound waves is constructive, the sound is louder than either of the two

original sounds. _____true_____

17. The study and description of how well sound can be heard in a

particular room or hall is called _____acoustics_____.

18. Circle the letter of the term that describes the repeated changes in
loudness that occurs when sound waves interfere both constructively
and destructively.

a. frequency   (**b.**)beats   **c.** tuners   **d.** intervals

19. What does a piano tuner do when he or she hears beats? ___The piano___

tuner adjusts the piano string until no beats are heard.
_____

CHAPTER 8, Sound *(continued)*

 ## Reading Skill Practice

You can often increase your understanding of what you've read by making comparisons. A compare/contrast table helps you to do this. On a separate sheet of paper, draw a table to compare the different instruments in *Exploring Making Music* on pages 238–239. List the five instruments to be compared across the top of your table. Then list the characteristics that will form the basis of your comparison in the left-hand column. These characteristics should include *Major Group, How Music Is Produced,* and *How Pitch Is Changed.* For more information about compare/contrast tables, see page 832 in the Skills Handbook of your textbook.

Students should complete the table with information about the violin, clarinet, harp, electronic keyboard, and French horn.

• •

SECTION 8-4 ## How You Hear Sound
(pages 244-246)

This section describes how you hear sound and explains what causes hearing loss.

▶ How You Hear Sound (pages 244–245)

Match the three main sections of the ear with their functions.

Main Section	Function
__b__ **1.** outer ear	**a.** Transmits sound waves inward
__a__ **2.** middle ear	**b.** Funnels sound waves
__c__ **3.** inner ear	**c.** Converts sound waves into a form the brain can understand

4. The outermost part of your ear collects sound waves and directs them into a narrower region known as the ____ear canal____.

5. What is the eardrum and where is it located? ___It is a small, tightly___ stretched, drumlike membrane at the end of the ear canal. _____

_____

6. What cavity of the inner ear is filled with fluid? ___the cochlea___

Science Explorer *Focus on Physical Science*

© Prentice-Hall, Inc.

7. What part of the ear contains the three smallest bones in your body?

   _____ middle ear _____

▶ Hearing Loss (page 246)

8. Circle the letter of each cause of hearing loss.

   (a.) aging   (b.) injury   c. nerve fibers   (d.) infection

9. Why is it dangerous to put objects into your ear, even to clean it?

   Your eardrum could be damaged or punctured, which could cause hearing

   loss.

10. How can a viral or bacterial infection cause hearing loss? __It can__

    damage the delicate inner ear.

11. What is the most common type of hearing loss? __The most common__

    type is hearing loss due to aging, in which the tiny hair cells in the cochlea

    become less effective in detecting signals.

12. When you know you are going to be exposed to loud noises, what

    should you do to prevent hearing loss? __You should wear ear plugs or__

    use other hearing protection.

13. Is the following sentence true or false? Hearing aids are amplifiers.

    _____ true _____

· ·

SECTION 8–5 Applications of Sound (pages 248–252)

This section explains how sound waves are used to tell distances. It also describes how animals use sounds and how sound is used in medicine.

▶ Reflection of Sound Waves (page 248)

1. A reflected sound wave is called a(n) __echo__.

CHAPTER 8, Sound *(continued)*

2. What does a sound wave do when it hits a surface through which it

cannot pass? <u>It bounces back, or reflects.</u>

_____

▶ Sonar (page 249)

3. Circle the letter of the following that are uses of reflected sound waves.

a. To raise a sunken ship to the surface of water

b. To determine the depth of water

c. To locate boats out on the ocean

d. To find schools of fish

4. What is sonar? <u>Sonar is a system of detecting reflected sound waves.</u>

_____

5. Complete the flowchart about how sonar works in calculating the depth
of the ocean.

```
┌─────────────────────────────────────────────┐
│  A sonar machine sends a burst of ultrasound  │
│        sound waves                            │
│  _____ through the water.│
└─────────────────────────────────────────────┘
                     │
                     ▼
┌─────────────────────────────────────────────┐
│  When the sound waves hit the ocean floor, they│
│                    reflect                     │
│  bounce back, or _____.          │
└─────────────────────────────────────────────┘
                     │
                     ▼
┌─────────────────────────────────────────────┐
│  The reflected sound waves are detected by the │
│           sonar machine                        │
│  _____.                  │
└─────────────────────────────────────────────┘
                     │
                     ▼
┌─────────────────────────────────────────────┐
│                           time                 │
│  The sonar machine measures the _____  │
│  it takes to detect the reflected sound waves. │
└─────────────────────────────────────────────┘
```

6. What does the intensity of the reflected sound waves tell the sonar machine about the object that reflected the waves? _The intensity tells_ _the size and shape of the object._

_____

▶ Uses of Ultrasound and Infrasound (pages 250–252)

7. Is the following sentence true or false? Some animals communicate using sounds with frequencies that humans cannot hear. _____true_____

8. The use of sound waves to determine distances or to locate objects is called _____echolocation_____.

9. Describe how a bat uses echolocation to avoid bumping into an object as it flies. _A bat sends out pulses of sound. Then it listens to how long the_ _sound takes to return. By picking up the echoes, the bat can tell if it is about_ _to bump into something._

_____

10. A picture of the inside of the human body using ultrasound is called a(n) _____sonogram_____.

11. In Figure 25 on page 251, what is the doctor trying to see with the ultrasound machine? _The doctor is trying to see the developing baby_ _inside the pregnant woman._

_____

12. What are three examples of common household objects that use ultrasound waves? _Electric toothbrush, ultrasonic jewelry cleaner,_ _automatic focus camera_

_____

CHAPTER 8, Sound *(continued)*

WordWise

Use the clues to help you unscramble the key terms from Chapter 8. Then put the numbered letters in order to find the answer to the riddle.

Clues	Key Terms	
The membrane that separates the outer ear from the middle ear	mrrudae	e a r d r u m (1 under e)
The cavity filled with liquid in the inner ear	ccleoah	c o c h l e a (2 under c)
How high or low a sound seems to a person	hctip	p i t c h (3 under h)
Sound waves with frequencies above the normal human range of hearing	dnuosartlu	u l t r a s o u n d (4 under o)
The ability of a material to bounce back after being disturbed	ttiiscyale	e l a s t i c i t y (5 under l)
A mixture of sound waves that do not sound pleasing together	ensoi	n o i s e (6 under o)
How well sounds can be heard in a particular room or hall	ccuossiat	a c o u s t i c s (7 under c)
Your voice box	xyarnl	l a r y n x (8 under a)
The quality of the sound you hear	erbmit	t i m b r e (9 under t)
Sound with a pleasing timbre and clear pitch	smcui	m u s i c (10 under i)
The sound produced when tones are played together that seem to have no musical relationship	sseaionncd	d i s s o n a n c e (11 under o)
The amount of energy a sound wave carries per second through a unit area	ynittiens	i n t e n s i t y (12 under s)

Riddle: What is the use of sound to find distance?

Answer: e c h o l o c a t i o n
1 2 3 4 5 6 7 8 9 10 11 12

© Prentice-Hall, Inc.

CHAPTER 9

THE ELECTROMAGNETIC SPECTRUM

···

SECTION 9–1 The Nature of Electromagnetic Waves (pages 258–261)

This section explains what light is and describes how scientists explain properties of light.

▶ **Electromagnetic Waves** (pages 259–260)

1. What are electromagnetic waves? __They are transverse waves that have__ some electrical properties and some magnetic properties. _____

_____

2. Is the following sentence true or false? Electromagnetic waves can transfer energy only through a medium. _____false_____

3. What do electromagnetic waves consist of? __They consist of changing__ electric and magnetic fields. _____

_____

4. Complete the table about electric and magnetic fields.

Electric and Magnetic Fields	
Field	**Definition**
Electric field	A region in which charged particles can be pushed or pulled
Magnetic field	A region in which magnetic forces are present

5. The energy that is transferred by electromagnetic waves is called ____electromagnetic radiation____.

CHAPTER 9, The Electromagnetic Spectrum *(continued)*

6. Circle the letter of each sentence that is true about electric and magnetic fields.

    (a.) An electromagnetic wave occurs when electric and magnetic fields vibrate at right angles to each other.

    b. A magnetic field is surrounded by an electric current.

    (c.) When an electric field vibrates, so does the magnetic field.

    (d.) An electric current is surrounded by a magnetic field.

7. Is the following sentence true or false? All electromagnetic waves travel at the same speed. _____ true _____

▶ Waves or Particles? (pages 260–261)

8. Light has many of the properties of waves. But light can also act as though it is a stream of _____ particles _____.

9. What happens when light enters a polarizing filter? ___ Only some waves ___ can pass through.

10. The light that passes through a polarizing filter is called _____ polarized light _____.

11. When light passes through a polarizing filter, does it have the properties of a wave or a particle? _____ a wave _____

12. Is the following sentence true or false? If two polarizing filters are placed so that one is rotated 90° from the other, all light can come through. _____ false _____

13. The movement of electrons in a substance when light is shined on it is called the _____ photoelectric effect _____.

14. The photoelectric effect can only be explained by thinking of light as a stream of tiny packets of energy, or as _____ particles _____.

15. What are particles of light energy called? _____ photons _____

SECTION 9-2 Waves of the Electromagnetic Spectrum (pages 262-270)

This section explains how electromagnetic waves differ from one another. It also describes the different waves of the electromagnetic spectrum.

▶ Characteristics of Electromagnetic Waves (pages 262–263)

1. Circle the letter of each sentence that is true about electromagnetic waves.

   (a.) Different electromagnetic waves have different frequencies.

   b. All electromagnetic waves have the same wavelength.

   (c.) Different electromagnetic waves have different wavelengths.

   (d.) All electromagnetic waves travel at the same speed.

2. Circle the letter of each sentence that is true about electromagnetic waves.

   (a.) As the wavelength of electromagnetic waves decreases, the frequency increases.

   (b.) Waves with the longest wavelengths have the lowest frequencies.

   (c.) As the frequency of electromagnetic waves decreases, the wavelength increases.

   d. Waves with the shortest wavelengths have the lowest frequencies.

3. What is the name for the range of electromagnetic waves when they are

   placed in order of increasing frequency? _The electromagnetic spectrum_

   _____

4. Label the electromagnetic spectrum below with the names of the different waves that make up the spectrum.

Electromagnetic Spectrum

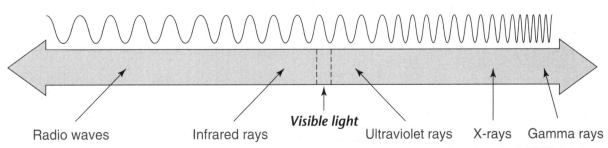

Radio waves   Infrared rays   *Visible light*   Ultraviolet rays   X-rays   Gamma rays

© Prentice-Hall, Inc.

CHAPTER 9, The Electromagnetic Spectrum (*continued*)

▶ **Radio Waves** (pages 263–265)

5. Each radio station in an area broadcasts at a different ____frequency____.

6. What does a radio convert radio waves into? ____sound____

7. Is the following sentence true or false? Microwaves are a kind of radio waves. ____true____

8. Circle the letter of the reason why you shouldn't put a metal object in a microwave oven.

   a. Microwaves can pass right through metal objects.

   b. Microwaves are easily blocked by buildings.

   (c.) Microwaves cause a buildup of electrical energy in metal.

   d. Microwaves are easily absorbed into metal objects.

9. A system of detecting reflected microwaves to locate objects is called ____radar____.

10. What is the use of radio waves in medicine to produce pictures of tissues in the human body called? ____Magnetic resonance imaging, or MRI____

▶ **Infrared Rays** (pages 265–267)

11. The energy you feel as heat from an electric burner is electromagnetic waves called ____infrared rays____.

12. Circle the letter of each sentence that is true about infrared rays.

   (a.) Infrared rays have longer wavelengths than visible light.

   (b.) Most objects give off infrared rays.

   (c.) The longest infrared rays are sometimes called heat rays.

   d. Heat lamps give off no infrared rays.

13. A picture produced by an infrared camera using infrared rays is called a(n) ____thermogram____.

Science Explorer *Focus on Physical Science*

▶ Visible Light (page 268)

14. The part of the electromagnetic spectrum that you can see is called
_____ visible light _____.

15. Look at Figure 5 on page 263. What are the colors of light that make up visible light? Write their names from longest wavelength to shortest wavelength.

a. red _____ b. orange _____ c. yellow _____

d. green _____ e. blue _____ f. violet _____

16. Is the following sentence true or false? Most visible light is made up of a mixture of the colors in the visible spectrum. _____ true _____

▶ Ultraviolet Rays (pages 268–269)

17. Electromagnetic waves with wavelengths just shorter than those of visible light are called _____ ultraviolet rays _____.

18. Circle the letter of each sentence that is true about ultraviolet rays.

(a.) Too much exposure to UV rays can cause skin cancer.

b. Humans with good vision can see UV rays.

(c.) UV rays cause skin cells to produce vitamin D.

(d.) Lamps that produce UV rays are used to kill bacteria.

▶ X-Rays (page 269)

19. Electromagnetic waves with frequencies higher than ultraviolet rays but lower than gamma rays are _____ X-rays _____.

20. Circle the letter of the reason why bones show up as lighter areas on photographic plates in an X-ray machine.

(a.) Bones absorb X-rays and don't allow them to pass through.

b. X-rays pass right through skin and bones.

c. Bones cause the photographic plate in an X-ray machine to darken.

d. X-rays cannot pass through the skin above the photographic plates.

CHAPTER 9, The Electromagnetic Spectrum *(continued)*

▶ **Gamma Rays** (page 270)

21. The electromagnetic waves with the shortest wavelengths and the

highest frequencies are called _____ gamma rays _____.

22. Why are gamma rays the most penetrating of all the electromagnetic rays?

They have the greatest amount of energy.

_____

• •

SECTION 9–3 **Producing Visible Light**
(pages 272-275)

This section describes different kinds of light bulbs. It also identifies the colors of light produced by the most common kind of light bulb.

▶ **Introduction** (page 272)

1. Complete the table below by writing the correct term.

Kinds of Objects	
Kind of Object	**Description**
Illuminated object	An object that can be seen because it reflects light
Luminous object	An object that gives off its own light

2. To view the different colors of light produced by each type of light

bulb, you can use an instrument called a(n) _____ spectroscope _____.

▶ **Incandescent Lights** (pages 272-273)

3. A light that glows when a filament inside it gets hot is called a(n)

_____ incandescent light _____.

4. What is the filament inside a light bulb? ___ The filament is a thin wire coil. ___

_____

5. Circle the letter of each sentence that is true about incandescent lights.

(a.) Most of the energy produced by incandescent bulbs is given off as infrared rays.

(b.) Incandescent bulbs give off all the colors of visible light.

c. Incandescent bulbs are very efficient in giving off light.

(d.) Inventor Thomas Edison developed a long-lasting incandescent bulb.

6. Is the following sentence true or false? Less than ten percent of the energy used to operate an incandescent bulb is given out as light.

_____true_____

▶ Fluorescent Lights (page 273)

7. Lights that glow when an electric current causes ultraviolet waves to strike a coating inside a tube are called _____fluorescent lights_____.

8. The process of ultraviolet waves hitting the powder coating inside a fluorescent bulb and causing the coating to emit visible light is called

_____fluorescing_____.

9. Circle the letter of each sentence that is true about fluorescent lights.

(a.) Fluorescent lights give off most of their energy as light.

(b.) Each glass fluorescent-light tube contains a gas.

(c.) Fluorescent lights emit visible light when UV rays strike the powder coating on the inside of the glass tube.

d. Fluorescent lights usually don't last as long as incandescent lights.

▶ Neon Lights (page 274)

10. A sealed glass tube filled with neon gas that produces light is called a(n)

_____neon light_____.

11. Circle the letter of each sentence that is true about neon lights.

(a.) Neon lights are commonly used for bright, flashy signs.

(b.) Pure neon gives out red light.

c. Each glass neon-light tube is coated on the inside with a powder.

(d.) Often, what is called a neon light has a mixture of gases in the tube.

CHAPTER 9, The Electromagnetic Spectrum *(continued)*

▶ Sodium Vapor Lights (page 274)

12. Circle the letter of each sentence that is true about sodium vapor lights.

    (a.) Sodium vapor lights require very little electricity for a lot of light.

    (b.) In a sodium vapor light, heat from gases change sodium from a solid to a gas.

    c. Particles of sodium vapor give off a greenish blue light.

    (d.) Sodium vapor lights are often used for street lighting.

▶ Tungsten-Halogen Lights (page 275)

13. Circle the letter of each sentence that is true about tungsten-halogen lights.

    a. Tungsten-halogen lights work like fluorescent lights.

    (b.) The halogen gas in a tungsten-halogen light makes the filament give off a bright white light.

    (c.) In a tungsten-halogen light, a filament gets hot and glows.

    (d.) Halogen bulbs become very hot.

▶ Bioluminescence (page 275)

14. The process by which living organisms produce their own light with a

    chemical reaction is called _____ bioluminescence _____.

15. What are three kinds of organisms that produce light through

    bioluminescence? _Fireflies, jellyfish, and deep-sea fish_____

📖 Reading Skill Practice

A flowchart can help you remember the order in which events occur. Create a flowchart that describes how an electric current produces light in an incandescent light, as explained on pages 272–273 of your book. Create a second flowchart that describes how an electric current produces light in a fluorescent light, as explained on page 273 of your book. For more information on flowcharts, see page 833 in the Skills Handbook of your book. Do your work on a separate sheet of paper.

Students should make two flowcharts. Each should begin with an electric current passing into a bulb. Each should end with the production of light from the bulb. The steps between should reflect the processes described in the text.

Science Explorer *Focus on Physical Science*

SECTION 9-4 Wireless Communication (pages 278-285)

This section describes how radio waves are used in communication, how cellular phones and pagers work, and how satellites relay information.

▶ Radio and Television (pages 278–281)

1. Is the following sentence true or false? Both radio and television programs are transmitted by radio waves. _____true_____

2. Look at the radio dial shown in Figure 21 on page 279. What does each number on the dial represent? _Each number represents a different_ _frequency._

3. Rank the measurements below from highest to lowest frequency. Rank the highest as *1*.

   __3__ **a.** 1,030 kHz   __1__ **b.** 107 MHz

   __4__ **c.** 550 kHz   __2__ **d.** 95 MHz

4. What does AM stand for? _____amplitude modulation_____

5. Complete the flowchart below about the broadcast of AM radio.

   The radio station converts sound into ____electronic signals____.

   ↓

   These signals are converted into a pattern of changes in the ____amplitude____ of radio waves.

   ↓

   The radio station broadcasts the radio waves through the ____air____.

   ↓

   Your radio picks up the radio waves and converts them back into ____electronic signals____.

© Prentice-Hall, Inc.

CHAPTER 9, The Electromagnetic Spectrum *(continued)*

6. What does FM stand for? _____ frequency modulation _____

7. How do FM signals travel? _____ They travel as changes, or modulations, in _____
the frequency of the wave. _____

_____

8. Is the following sentence true or false? The frequencies of FM stations are much lower than the frequencies of AM stations. _____ false _____

9. Why can't FM waves travel as far as AM waves? _____ FM waves have more _____
energy than AM waves. As a result, FM waves pass through the atmosphere
instead of being reflected back. _____

_____

10. How are television broadcasts different than radio broadcasts?
Television broadcasts carry picture signals as well as sound.

_____

11. What are the two main bands of television wave frequencies?

a. _____ Very High Frequency (VHF) _____ **b.** _____ Ultra High Frequency (UHF) _____

▶ Cellular Telephones (page 281)

12. Circle the letter of the kind of radio waves that transmit signals from cellular telephones.

a. X-rays **b.** infrared rays **c.** gamma rays **(d.)** microwaves

13. In a cellular telephone system, what does each cell have? _____ Each cell has _____
its own transmitter and receiver. _____

▶ Cordless Telephones (page 282)

14. What kind of waves transmits the signals from the handset to the base

of a cordless telephone? _____ radio waves _____

Name _____ Date _____ Class _____

▶ Pagers (pages 282–283)

15. When you leave a message for a pager, how does the information get to the correct pager? _The information is first sent to a receiving station._ _There it is coded and sent as electromagnetic waves to the correct pager._

▶ Communications Satellites (pages 284–285)

16. Is the following sentence true or false? Communications satellites are remote-controlled spacecraft that orbit Earth. ___true___

17. Circle the letter of each sentence that is true about communications satellites.

  a. It is necessary to have more than one satellite in orbit for any given purpose.

  b. Communications satellites receive sound waves from Earth and send radio waves back to Earth.

  c. Most satellites strengthen the signals they receive before they send them back to Earth.

  d. Communications satellites can relay several signals at once.

18. How do satellite telephone systems affect long-distance telephone calls? _They make long-distance calls more easily available and less costly._

19. What do television networks use communications satellites for? _They use satellites to send signals to local stations across the country._

20. If you had a GPS receiver, what could you determine by receiving signals from the Global Positioning System? _You could determine your exact location on Earth, or even in the air._

© Prentice-Hall, Inc.

Science Explorer *Focus on Physical Science*

CHAPTER 9, The Electromagnetic Spectrum *(continued)*

WordWise

Complete the sentences by using one of the scrambled words below.

Word Bank

ouuilmns	mmargoerht	uoeescntrfl ghtsli	noothp tionaidar
oidar sevaw	yasr-X	cancentdesin ghtsil	andetimluli
iielbsv tighl	maggnii	eaoimcrwvs	

The energy that is transferred by electromagnetic waves is called electromagnetic

_____radiation_____.

Each tiny packet of light energy is called a(n) _____photon_____.

The radio waves with the longest wavelengths and lowest frequencies are called

_____radio waves_____.

The radio waves with the shortest wavelengths and the highest frequencies are

_____microwaves_____.

The process of using radio waves to produce pictures of tissues in the human body is

called magnetic resonance _____imaging_____.

A picture taken with an infrared camera that shows regions of different temperatures

in different colors is a(n) _____thermogram_____.

The part of the electromagnetic spectrum that you can see is called _____visible light_____.

Electromagnetic waves with wavelengths just a little higher than ultraviolet rays are

called _____X-rays_____.

An object that can be seen because it reflects light is said to be _____illuminated_____.

An object that gives off its own light is said to be _____luminous_____.

Lights that glow when a filament inside them gets hot are called _____incandescent lights_____.

Lights that glow when an electric current causes ultraviolet waves to strike a coating

inside a tube are called _____fluorescent lights_____.

CHAPTER 10

LIGHT

· ·

SECTION 10-1 **Reflection and Mirrors** (pages 294-298)

This section describes what happens when light strikes an object and identifies three kinds of mirrors.

▶ When Light Strikes an Object (page 294)

1. What three things can occur when light strikes an object? __It can be__

reflected, absorbed, or transmitted. _____

_____

2. Complete the table about kinds of objects.

Kinds of Objects		
Object	**Description**	**Examples**
Transparent	A material that transmits light	Clear glass, water, air
Translucent	A material that scatters light as it passes through	Frosted glass, wax paper
Opaque	A material that reflects or absorbs all of the light that strikes it	Wood, metal, cotton, wool

▶ Kinds of Reflection (page 295)

3. To show how light travels and reflects, you can represent light waves as

straight lines called ____rays____.

CHAPTER 10, Light *(continued)*

4. What occurs when parallel rays of light hit a smooth surface? __Regular__ reflection occurs.

5. What occurs when parallel rays of light hit a bumpy, or uneven, surface?
Diffuse reflection occurs.

_____

▶ Mirrors (pages 296–298)

6. What is a mirror? __A mirror is a sheet of glass that has a smooth, silver-__ colored coating on the back side.

_____

7. A copy of an object formed by reflected or refracted rays of light is a(n) _____image_____.

8. What size of image does a plane mirror produce? __same-size image__

9. An upright image formed where rays of light appear to meet behind a mirror is called a(n) _____virtual image_____.

10. The point at which light rays meet is called the _____focal point_____.

11. An image formed when rays actually meet at a point is called a(n) _____real image_____.

12. Complete the table about kinds of mirrors.

Kinds of Mirrors			
Kind of Mirror	**Description**	**Virtual or Real Image?**	**Upright or Inverted?**
Plane mirror	Flat	Virtual	Upright
Concave mirror	Curved inward	Virtual or real	Inverted or upright
Convex mirror	Curved outward	Virtual	Upright

© Prentice-Hall, Inc.

Science Explorer *Focus on Physical Science*

Refraction and Lenses (pages 299-303)

This section explains what happens when light rays enter a medium at an angle. It also describes how images are formed when light is refracted by transparent material.

▶ Refraction of Light (pages 299–301)

1. When light rays enter a new medium at an angle, what does the change in speed cause the rays to do? The change in speed causes the rays to bend, or change direction.

2. Rank the following mediums according to how fast light travels through them. Rank the fastest as *1*.

   _____2_____ **a.** water   _____3_____ **b.** glass   _____1_____ **c.** air

3. What is a material's index of refraction? It is a measure of how much a ray of light bends when it enters the material.

4. Glass causes light to bend more than air does. Which material has a higher index of refraction? _____glass_____

5. What does Figure 9 on page 300 show happens to white light when it enters a prism? The prism causes white light to separate into its component colors.

6. Explain why a rainbow can form when light shines through tiny raindrops of water. Raindrops act like tiny prisms, refracting and reflecting the light and separating the colors.

CHAPTER 10, Light (continued)

7. An image of a distant object caused by the refraction of light is called

a(n) _____mirage_____.

▶ Lenses (pages 302–303)

8. A curved piece of glass or other transparent material that is used to

refract light is called a(n) _____lens_____.

9. How does a lens form an image? ___A lens forms an image by refracting___

__light rays that pass through it.__

_____

10. Label each lens as either a convex lens or a concave lens. Then show
    what happens to the light rays as they pass through each lens.

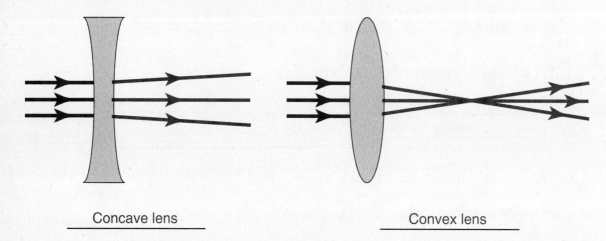

_____Concave lens_____   _____Convex lens_____

11. Complete the following table about lenses.

Kinds of Lenses		
Shape of Lens	**Description**	**Image Formed—Real or Virtual?**
Concave	Thinner in the center than at the edges	Virtual
Convex	Thicker in the center than at the edges	Real or virtual

SECTION 10-3 Color (pages 305-309)

This section explains what determines the color of an object. It also identifies the primary colors of light and explains how mixing colored substances is different from mixing light.

▶ The Color of Objects (pages 305–307)

1. The color of an object is the color of the light it _____reflects_____.

2. Complete the flowchart about why you see the petals of a lily as orange.

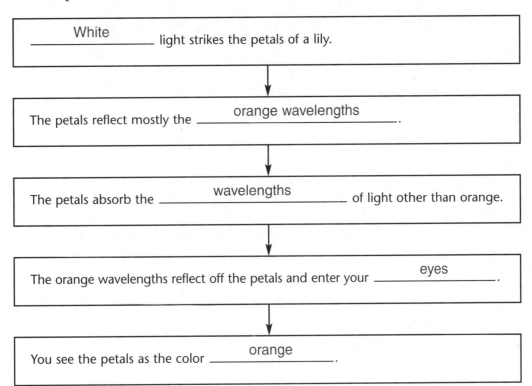

_____White_____ light strikes the petals of a lily.

The petals reflect mostly the _____orange wavelengths_____.

The petals absorb the _____wavelengths_____ of light other than orange.

The orange wavelengths reflect off the petals and enter your _____eyes_____.

You see the petals as the color _____orange_____.

3. What do you see when white light strikes a material that reflects all the colors, such as a skunk's stripe? _____You see white light._____

_____

4. What do you see when white light strikes a material that absorbs all the colors, such as a skunk's body? _____You see black._____

_____

CHAPTER 10, Light *(continued)*

5. Is the following sentence true or false? Objects can look a different color depending on the color of light in which they are seen.

_____true_____

6. Circle the letter of the color of light that a red filter allows to pass through it.

     a. blue   b. magenta   c. cyan   (d.)red

▶ Combining Colors (pages 307–309)

7. The three colors that can be used to make any other color are called

_____primary colors_____.

8. Any two primary colors combined in equal amounts produce

_____secondary colors_____.

9. What are the three primary colors?

     a. red_____ b. green_____ c. blue_____

10. When combined in equal amounts, what do the primary colors of light

produce? _____white light_____

11. Complete the following "equations" by writing the secondary color the two primary colors of light produce.

     a. Green + Blue = _____Cyan_____

     b. Red + Green = _____Yellow_____

     c. Red + Blue = _____Magenta_____

12. Any two colors of light that combine to form white light are called

_____complementary colors_____.

13. What are pigments? _____Pigments are substances that are used to color_____

_____other materials._____

_____

14. Complete the following "equations" by writing the secondary color the two primary colors of pigments produce.

a. Magenta + Cyan = _____Blue_____

b. Magenta + Yellow = _____Red_____

c. Cyan + Yellow = _____Green_____

· ·

SECTION 10-4 Seeing Light (pages 311-314)

This section explains how your eyes allow you to see. It also describes what kinds of lenses are used to correct vision problems.

▶ The Human Eye (pages 312-313)

Match the part of the eye with its description.

	Part of Eye	Description
_b_	**1.** Cornea	**a.** The hole through which light enters the eye
_d_	**2.** Iris	**b.** The transparent front surface of the eye
_a_	**3.** Pupil	**c.** The short, thick nerve through which signals travel to the brain
_e_	**4.** Lens	**d.** The ring of colored muscle around the pupil
_f_	**5.** Retina	**e.** The curved part behind the pupil that refracts light
_c_	**6.** Optic nerve	**f.** The layer of cells lining the inside of the eyeball

7. What do your eyelids do for your eyes each time you blink? __They__ clean and moisten the cornea. _____

_____

8. What part gives the eye its color? _____the iris_____

9. Why does the pupil look black? __It is an opening into the dark inside of__ the eye. _____

CHAPTER 10, Light *(continued)*

10. What is the retina made up of? It's made up of millions of tiny, light-
sensitive cells called rods and cones.

_____

11. The cells of the retina that distinguish among black, white, and shades
of gray are called _____rods_____ .

12. The cells of the retina that respond to colors are called _____cones_____ .

13. Label the parts of the eye on the illustration.

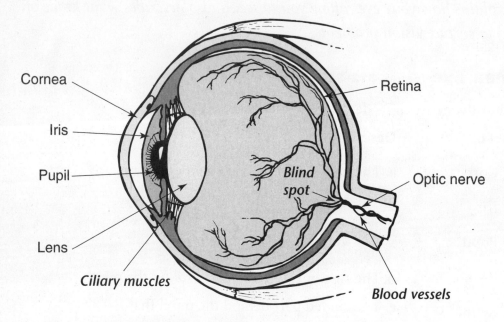

Cornea

Iris

Pupil

Lens

Ciliary muscles

Blind spot

Retina

Optic nerve

Blood vessels

▶ Correcting Vision (pages 313–314)

14. Complete the table about correcting vision.

Correcting Vision			
Vision Problem	**Shape of Eyeball**	**Vision Perception**	**Type of Correction Lens**
Nearsightedness	A little too long	Distant objects appear blurry	Concave
Farsightedness	A little too short	Nearby objects appear blurry	Convex

Reading Skill Practice

An outline can help you remember the main points of a section in the order in which they appear. Write an outline of Section 10–4. The title of your outline should be the same as the title of the section. Use the section's major headings for your major topics. Use the section's subheadings for your subtopics. List details about each subtopic under your subheadings. When you finish, you'll have an outline of the section. Do your work on a separate sheet of paper.

Students' outlines should match the headings of Section 10–4. Major headings are *The Human Eye* and *Correcting Vision.* Under each subhead, students should list two or three important details.

SECTION 10-5 Using Light (pages 315-324)

This section describes how telescopes, microscopes, and cameras work. It also explains how a special kind of light differs from ordinary light.

▶ Telescopes (page 316)

1. An instrument that forms enlarged images of distant objects and makes them appear closer is called a(n) _____telescope_____.

2. What is the most common use of telescopes? __To collect light from space__

   _____

3. Complete the table about telescopes.

Kinds of Telescopes		
Type of Telescope	**Lenses or Mirrors?**	**Image You See—Upright or Upside Down?**
Refracting telescope	Lenses	Upside down
Reflecting telescope	Mirrors	Upside down

4. What does the objective lens of a refracting telescope do? __It gathers light__ from an object and focuses the rays to form a real image.

CHAPTER 10, Light *(continued)*

5. What does the eyepiece lens of a refracting telescope do? __It magnifies__

the image so you can see it clearly. _____

_____

▶ Microscopes (page 317)

6. An instrument that uses a combination of lenses to produce enlarged

images of tiny objects is called a(n) _____microscope_____.

7. On a microscope, what is the function of the objective lens? __It forms a__

real, but enlarged, image of a tiny object. _____

_____

▶ Cameras (pages 317–318)

8. An instrument that uses lenses to focus light and record an image of an

object is called a(n) _____camera_____.

9. What happens when you press the button of a camera? __The shutter__

briefly opens, allowing light to hit the film. _____

_____

10. How is the diaphragm of a camera like the iris of an eye? __The_____

diaphragm controls the amount of light that enters the camera through the

aperture. Similarly, the iris controls the amount of light that enters the eye

through the pupil. _____

▶ Lasers (pages 318–319)

11. What is a device called that produces coherent light, which consists of

light waves that all have the same wavelength? _____a laser_____

12. In a laser beam, the crests and troughs of all the waves

_____align_____ with each other.

© Prentice-Hall, Inc.

13. What does a laser consist of? <u>A laser consists of a tube that contains a</u>

<u>material such as ruby or a helium-neon mixture.</u>

_____

▶ Uses of Lasers (pages 320–322)

14. Circle the letter of each sentence that is true about the uses of lasers.

(**a.**)Some lasers are used to cut through steel.

(**b.**)A laser beam is used to play compact discs, or CDs.

c. A laser beam is used as a tunnel between England and France.

(**d.**)Doctors use lasers in surgery.

15. What is a hologram? <u>A hologram is a three-dimensional photograph</u>

<u>created by using the light from a laser.</u>

_____

▶ Optical Fibers (pages 322–324)

16. Is the following sentence true or false? Laser beams can carry signals by

modulation like radio waves. <u>true</u>

17. What are optical fibers? <u>They are long, thin strands of glass or plastic</u>

<u>that can carry light for long distances without allowing the light to fade out.</u>

_____

18. The complete reflection of light by the inside surface of a medium is

called <u>total internal reflection</u>.

19. Circle the letter of each sentence that is true about the uses of optical
fibers.

a. An optical fiber can carry only one telephone call at a time.

(**b.**)Doctors use optical fibers to examine internal organs.

(**c.**)Optical fibers are much thinner than copper wire.

(**d.**)Optical fibers have led to great improvements in computer networks.

Name _____ Date _____ Class _____

CHAPTER 10, Light *(continued)*

WordWise

Answer the questions by writing the correct key terms in the blanks. Use the circled letter in each term to find the hidden key term. Then write a definition for the hidden key term.

What is a curved piece of glass or other transparent material that is used to refract light? l e (n) s

What is a copy of an object formed by reflected or refracted rays of light?
i m a g (e)

What is an instrument called that uses lenses to focus light and record an image of an object? c (a) m e r a

What is the transparent front surface of the eye called? c o (r) n e a

What is a device called that produces coherent light, which consists of light waves that all have the same wavelength? l a (s) e r

What is an instrument called that uses a combination of lenses to produce enlarged images of tiny objects? m (i) c r o s c o p e

What are substances called that are used to color other materials?
p i (g) m e n t s

What is a person called who can see distant objects clearly, but nearby objects appear blurry? f a r s i g (h) t e d

What is the layer of cells that line the inside of the eyeball called? r e (t) i n a

What is a material called that reflects or absorbs all of the light that strikes it?
o p a q u (e)

What is the measure of how much a ray of light bends when it enters the material called? i n (d) e x o f r e f r a c t i o n

Hidden Term: n e a r s i g h t e d

Definition: _A nearsighted person is someone who can see nearby things clearly, but objects at a distance appear blurry._

Science Explorer *Focus on Physical Science*

CHAPTER 11

MAGNETISM AND ELECTROMAGNETISM

SECTION 11–1 **The Nature of Magnetism** (pages 336–343)

This sections describes magnets and explains the magnetic force around magnets. It also describes the inside of magnets.

▶ Magnets (page 337)

1. Circle the letter of the mineral that magnetic rocks contain.

   (a.) magnetite   **b.** manganese   **c.** lodestone   **d.** lignite

2. What is magnetism? ___Magnetism is the attraction of a magnet for another___

   ___object.___

▶ Magnetic Poles (pages 337–338)

3. Any magnet, no matter what its shape, has two ends, each one called

   a(n) _____magnetic pole_____.

4. Circle the letter of each sentence that is true about magnetic poles.

   (a.) One pole of a magnet will point north.

   b. Both the north and the south pole always point north.

   c. Two north poles make up a pair of unlike, or opposite, poles.

   (d.) The pole that points south is labeled the south pole.

5. What happens if you break a magnet in two? ___You will have two___

   ___separate magnets.___

CHAPTER 11, Magnetism and Electromagnetism *(continued)*

6. Complete the table below by writing whether the magnets in each pair described in the first column will repel or attract each other.

Magnetic Attraction	
Situation	**Repel or Attract?**
Two south poles are brought together.	Repel
A north pole is brought to a south pole.	Attract
Two north poles are brought together.	Repel
A south pole is brought to a north pole.	Attract

▶ Magnetic Fields (pages 339–340)

7. The region of magnetic force around a magnet is known as its
_____magnetic field_____.

8. What are the lines called that map out the magnetic field around a
magnet? _____magnetic field lines_____

9. Draw a magnetic field around the illustration of the bar magnet shown here.

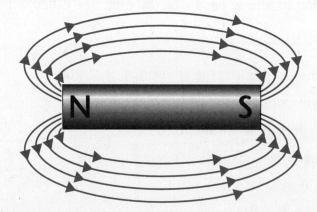

10. When the magnetic fields of two or more magnets overlap, what is the
result? _____The result is a combined magnetic field._____

_____

▶ Inside a Magnet (pages 340–341)

11. What do the magnetic properties of a material depend on? __They__ depend on the structure of the material's atoms. _____

_____

12. The smallest particle of an element that has the properties of that element is called a(n) _____atom_____ .

13. One of about 100 basic materials that make up all matter is called a(n) _____element_____ .

14. What is the central core of an atom called? _____nucleus_____

15. What is the difference between protons and electrons? __Protons are__ nuclear particles that carry a positive charge, whereas electrons orbit the nucleus and carry a negative charge. _____

_____

16. A cluster of billions of atoms that all have magnetic fields that are lined up in the same way is known as a(n) _____magnetic domain_____ .

17. How are magnetic domains arranged differently in magnetized material and in material that is not magnetized? __In magnetized material, all or__ most of the domains are arranged in the same direction. In material that is not magnetized, the domains point in random directions. _____

_____

_____

18. What is a ferromagnetic material? __It is a material that shows strong__ magnetic effects. _____

_____

CHAPTER 11, Magnetism and Electromagnetism *(continued)*

▶ Making Magnets (page 342)

19. What are two ways to make a magnet from an unmagnetized

    ferromagnetic material? _This can be done by placing the unmagnetized_

    material in a strong magnetic field or by rubbing it with one pole of a strong

    magnet.

20. A magnet made of a material that keeps its magnetism is called a(n)

    _____permanent magnet_____.

▶ Destroying Magnets (page 343)

21. What might happen if you drop a permanent magnet or strike it hard?

    Its domains could be knocked out of alignment, which would make it

    become unmagnetized.

22. Is the following sentence true or false? Above a certain temperature, a

    material loses the property of ferromagnetism. _____true_____

▶ Breaking Magnets (page 343)

23. Suppose you break a magnet into four pieces. What will be the

    magnetic properties of each piece? _Each piece retains its magnetic_

    properties.

Reading Skill Practice

Writing a summary can help you remember the information you have read. When you write a summary, write only the most important points. Write a summary of the information under the heading *Inside a Magnet* on pages 341–342. Your summary should be shorter than the text on which it is based. Do your work on a separate sheet of paper.

Students's summaries should consist of a paragraph that mentions all the highlighted words under the heading and emphasizes the highlighted sentence about magnetic domains.

SECTION 11-2 Magnetic Earth (pages 346-351)

This section identifies the magnetic properties of Earth and describes the effects of Earth's magnetic field.

▶ Introduction (page 346)

1. What is a compass? __A compass is a device that has a magnetized needle__ that can spin freely.

_____

2. Which way does a compass needle usually point? ____north____

▶ Earth As a Magnet (page 347)

3. How is Earth like a bar magnet? __Both have magnetic fields surrounding__ them.

_____

4. The poles of a magnetized needle on a compass align themselves with Earth's ____magnetic field____ .

▶ Magnetic Declination (pages 347–349)

5. Circle the letters of the two answers that name the same place on Earth.

   (a.) geographic north pole

   b. geographic south pole

   c. magnetic north pole

   (d.) true north

6. Is the following sentence true or false? The magnetic poles are not located exactly at the geographic poles. ____true____

7. The angle between a line to the geographic north pole and a line to the magnetic north pole is known as ____magnetic declination____ .

CHAPTER 11, Magnetism and Electromagnetism *(continued)*

▶ The Magnetosphere (pages 349–350)

8. The doughnut-shaped regions 1,000–25,000 kilometers above Earth are called the ___Van Allen belts___.

9. What do the Van Allen belts contain? ___They contain electrons and protons traveling at very high speeds.___

10. The stream of electrically charged particles flowing at high speeds from the sun is called the ___solar wind___.

11. Circle the letter of the sentence that explains Earth's magnetosphere.

    a. The doughnut-shaped region 1,000 kilometers above Earth

    b. The region of Earth's magnetic field shaped by the solar wind

    c. The region between the geographic north pole and the magnetic north pole

    d. The region of Earth's magnetic field in the Van Allen belts

12. What is an aurora? ___It is a glowing region in the atmosphere caused by charged particles from the sun.___

13. Complete the flowchart about what causes the Northern Lights.

    ┌───┐
    │ Particles from the solar wind penetrate Earth's ___magnetic field___. │
    └───┘
                              ↓
    ┌───┐
    │ The particles follow the lines of Earth's magnetic field to the magnetic ___north pole___. │
    └───┘
                              ↓
    ┌───┐
    │ When the particles get close to the surface, they interact with atoms in the ___atmosphere___. │
    └───┘
                              ↓
    ┌───┐
    │ The interaction causes the atoms to give off glowing ___light___. │
    └───┘

▶ **Effects of Earth's Magnetic Field** (pages 350–351)

14. How could Earth's magnetic field magnetize an iron bar over many years?

If the iron bar were left lying in a north-south direction, Earth's magnetic field

could attract the domains in the bar strongly enough to cause them to line

up in the same direction.

_____

15. The magnetic record in the rock on the ocean floor depends on when

the rock was _____formed_____.

16. Is the following sentence true or false? Earth's magnetic field has

reversed direction every million years or so. _____true_____

. . . .

SECTION 11–3 **Electric Current and Magnetic Fields**
(pages 352–357)

This section explains how an electric current is related to a magnetic field. It also describes some characteristics of electric currents.

▶ **Electric Current** (pages 352–353)

Match each particle with its electric charge.

Particle	Electric Charge
__a__ **1.** electron	**a.** negative
__b__ **2.** proton	**b.** positive

3. The flow of electric charges through a material is called

_____electric current_____.

4. How is the rate at which an electric current flows determined? ___It is the___

amount of charge that passes through a wire in a unit of time.

_____

CHAPTER 11, Magnetism and Electromagnetism *(continued)*

5. Circle the letter of each of the following that stands for the unit of current.

   (a.) A   (b.) ampere   c. aurora   (d.) amp

6. Is the following sentence true or false? The number of amps tells the amount of charge flowing past a given point each second.

   _____ true _____

7. An electric current produces a(n) _____ electric field _____.

8. Look at Figure 17 on page 353. Why are the compass directions different in Figure 17B than in Figure 17C? _____ The direction of the electric current in Figure 17C is the reverse of the direction in Figure 17B. If the current is reversed, the magnetic field reverses as well. _____

▶ Moving Charge and Magnetism (page 353)

9. What causes all magnetism? _____ All magnetism is caused by the movement of charges. _____

▶ Electric Circuits (pages 354–355)

10. What is an electric circuit? _____ It is a complete path through which electric charges can flow. _____

11. What are the three basic features all electric circuits must have?

   a. _____ A source of electrical energy _____

   b. _____ Devices that are run by electrical energy _____

   c. _____ Conducting wires and a switch that connect the circuit _____

12. What does a source of electrical energy do in an electrical circuit?

It makes charges move around the circuit.

13. When a switch in an electrical circuit is closed, is the circuit complete

or broken? _____complete_____

14. On the circuit diagram shown here, label the switch, the resistor, and
the energy source.

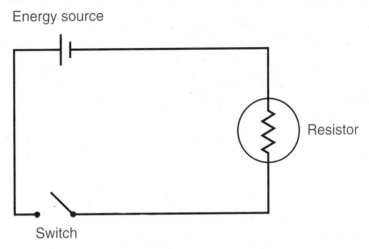

Energy source

Resistor

Switch

▶ Conductors and Insulators (page 354)

15. Complete the table about conductors and insulators.

Conductors and Insulators		
Material	**Description**	**Examples**
Conductors	Electric currents move freely through these materials.	Copper, silver, iron, aluminum
Insulators	Electric currents are not able to move freely through these materials.	Rubber, glass, sand, plastic, wood

▶ Electrical Resistance (pages 356–357)

16. A device that uses electrical energy as it interferes with, or resists, the

flow of charge is called a(n) _____resistor_____.

17. Circle the letter of each of the following that could be a resistor in an
electrical circuit.

    a. computer   **b.** switch   **c.** battery   **d.** light bulb

CHAPTER 11, Magnetism and Electromagnetism *(continued)*

18. What is resistance? _Resistance is the opposition to the movement of_ _____ charges flowing through a material.

_____

19. Within a material, what results in the conversion of an electron's energy to thermal energy and electromagnetic energy? _The collision of an_ _____ electron with particles in a material results in the conversion of an electron's energy.

20. Why did Thomas Edison decide to use tungsten when he developed his electric light bulb? _Tungsten is a metal that can get hot enough to glow_ without melting.

21. What is a superconductor? _A superconductor is a material that has no_ _____ electrical resistance.

_____

. . . .

SECTION 11-4

Electromagnets
(pages 360-362)

This section describes the characteristics of strong magnets that can be turned on and off.

▶ **Solenoids (pages 360–361)**

1. Is the following sentence true or false? The strength of a magnetic field decreases as the number of loops in a wire increases. _false_ _____

2. Suppose you wind a current-carrying wire into a coil. How have you changed the wire's magnetic field? _You have strengthened the magnetic_ field in the center of the coil.

_____

© Prentice-Hall, Inc.

3. A current-carrying wire with many loops is called a(n) _____solenoid_____.

4. How could you turn off a solenoid's magnetic field? __You could turn it__ off by switching the current off.

▶ Multiplying Magnetism (page 361)

5. Is the following sentence true or false? When iron is placed within a solenoid's magnetic field, the iron becomes a magnet. _____true_____

6. What is an electromagnet? __An electromagnet is a solenoid with a__ ferromagnetic core.

7. In an electromagnet, what produces the temporary magnetic field? The current in the wire and the magnetized core produces the magnetic field.

▶ Increasing the Strength of An Electromagnet (page 362)

8. Describe three ways you can increase the strength of an electromagnet.

   a. You can increase the current.

   b. You can add more loops of wire to the solenoid.

   c. You can use a stronger ferromagnetic material for the core.

▶ Recording Information (page 362)

9. Is the following sentence true or false? When you record information on a computer disk, you are using electromagnets. _____true_____

10. When you talk into a microphone, the variations in your voice are changed into variations in a(n) _____electric current_____.

CHAPTER 11, Magnetism and Electromagnetism *(continued)*

WordWise

Complete the crossword puzzle by using the clues below.

¹s	o	l	²e	n	o	i	d			
			l					³r		
⁴r		⁵n	e					e		
e		u	⁶c	o	m	p	a	s	s	
s		c	t			⁷a		i		
i		l	r			a		s		
⁸s	u	p	e	r	c	o	n	d	u	c	t	o	r

Clues Across

1. A current-carrying coil of wire with many loops
6. A device that has a magnetized needle that can spin freely
8. A material that has no electrical resistance
9. The smallest particle of an element that has the properties of that element
10. The region of Earth's magnetic field shaped by the solar wind

Clues Down

2. A solenoid with a ferromagnetic core
3. A device in an electric circuit that uses electrical energy as it interferes with the flow of electric charge
4. The opposition to the movement of charges flowing through a material
5. The central core of every atom
7. A glowing region of the atmosphere caused by charged particles from the sun

CHAPTER 12

ELECTRIC CHARGES AND CURRENT

· ·

SECTION 12-1 **Electric Charge and Static Electricity**
(pages 368-375)

This section describes how electric charges interact. It also explains static electricity.

▶ Types of Electric Charge (pages 368–369)

1. Why do protons repel protons but attract electrons? _Protons and_
   electrons have different types of charges.

2. The charge on a proton is called ___positive___.

3. The charge on an electron is called ___negative___.

▶ Interactions Between Charges (page 369)

4. Circle the letter of each statement that is true about interactions between charges.

   (a.) Charges that are the same repel each other.

   b. Charged objects never attract each other.

   (c.) Charges that are different attract each other.

   d. Charged objects always repel each other.

▶ Electric Fields (pages 369–370)

5. The field around electrically charged particles that exerts a force on

   other charged particles is called a(n) ___electric field___.

6. What happens when a charged particle is placed in the electric field of

   another particle with the same charge? _It is pulled toward the other_
   particle.

CHAPTER 12, Electric Charges and Current (continued)

7. Electric field lines are drawn with arrows to show the direction of the

   force on a(n) _____positive charge_____ .

8. Is the following sentence true or false? When two charged particles
   come near each other, the electric field of only one of the particles is

   altered. _____false_____

▶ Static Charge (pages 370–372)

9. Circle the letter of the sentence that explains why there is no overall
   electrical force in a neutral object.

   a. In the object's atoms, each positive charge is balanced by a negative
   charge.

   b. The object's atoms contain no charged particles.

   c. The positive charges are attracted to other positive charges.

   d. In the object's atoms, negative charges outnumber positive charges.

10. How can a neutral object become charged? ___It can become charged by___

    gaining or losing electrons. _____

    _____

11. If an object gains electrons, what will be its overall charge?

    _____negative_____

12. The buildup of charges on an object is called ___static electricity___ .

13. Complete the table about methods of transferring charge.

Transferring Charges	
Method	**Definition**
Fiction	The transfer of electrons from one object to another by rubbing
Induction	The movement of electrons to one part of an object by the electric field of another object
Conduction	The transfer of electrons from a charged object to another object by direct contact

© Prentice-Hall, Inc.

Science Explorer *Focus on Physical Science*

14. What law states that charges are not created or destroyed? The law of
conservation of charge

15. Suppose you dry your clothes in a dryer, and when you take them out
they cling to one another. Why do they stick together? In a dryer,
electrons from one fabric rub off onto another. In this way, the clothes
become charged. A positively charged fabric is then attracted to a negatively
charged fabric.

▶ Static Discharge (pages 372–374)

16. What happens when a negatively charged object and a positively
charged object are brought together? Electrons move until both objects
have the same charge.

17. The loss of static electricity as electric charges move off an object is
called static discharge.

18. On a humid day, what molecules might carry off extra electrons and
prevent the buildup of charges on objects? water molecules

19. Is the following sentence true or false? Lightning is an example of static
discharge. true

▶ Detecting Charge (page 375)

20. An electric charge can be detected by an instrument called a(n)
electroscope.

21. Why do the leaves of an electroscope spread apart when a charged
object touches the metal knob? The electric charge from the object
travels along the rod and into or out of the leaves. Since the charge on both
leaves is the same, the leaves repel each other, or spread apart.

CHAPTER 12, Electric Charges and Current *(continued)*

📖 Reading Skill Practice

A flowchart can help you remember the order in which events occur. On a separate sheet of paper, create a flowchart that describes the steps that take place when lightning reaches Earth, as explained on page 374. The first event in your flowchart will be this: Negative charges on the bottom of a cloud repel electrons. For more information about flowcharts, see page 833 of the Skills Handbook in your textbook. Do your work on a separate sheet of paper.

Students' flowcharts may vary somewhat, but each should contain the information in the last three sentences of page 374.

SECTION 12-2 **Circuit Measurements** (pages 378-383)

This section explains what causes an electric current to flow. It also describes what an electric circuit needs to maintain an electric current.

▶ Electrical Potential (page 378)

1. The type of energy that depends on position is called ___potential energy___.

2. The potential energy in an electric circuit is related to the force exerted by ___electric fields___.

3. What is electrical potential? ___It is the potential energy per unit of electric charge.___

▶ Voltage (page 379)

4. The difference in electrical potential between two places is called the ___potential difference___.

5. What is another name for potential difference? ___voltage___

6. What causes current to flow through an electric circuit?
___voltage___

▶ Voltage Sources (page 380)

7. What does a voltage source do in an electric circuit? _It creates a_

potential difference.

8. Circle the letter of each example of a voltage source.

   a. light bulb   **(b.)** generator   **c.** computer   **(d.)** battery

9. What does an increase in voltage cause in an electric circuit? _It causes_

   a greater flow of electric current.

   _____

10. Charges move around an electric circuit as the result of the potential

    difference between a voltage source's two _terminals_____.

▶ Resistance (pages 380–381)

11. Circle the letter of the two factors that affect the amount of current that
    flows through a circuit.

    (a.) voltage   **(b.)** resistance   **c.** switch   **d.** current

12. Is the following sentence true or false? The greater the resistance, the

    less current there is for a given voltage. _true_____

13. If an electric current can travel through two paths, which will it travel

    through? _It will travel through the path with the lower resistance._

    _____

▶ Ohm's Law (pages 382–383)

14. A device that measures potential difference, or voltage, is called a(n)

    _voltmeter_____.

15. What does an ammeter measure? _current_____

16. Is the following sentence true or false? The resistance of most
    conductors does not vary with the amount of voltage across them.

    _true_____

CHAPTER 12, Electric Charges and Current (continued)

17. What is the formula for Ohm's law?

Resistance = $\dfrac{\text{Voltage}}{\text{Current}}$

_____

18. If you know the current and the resistance in a circuit, what formula

would you use to find the voltage? V = IR _____

19. Write the unit of measure and its abbreviation for each value.

resistance: _____ohm Ω_____

voltage: _____volt V_____

current: _____ampere or amp A_____

20. Circle the letter of each sentence that is true if the resistance of a
conductor remains constant.

(a.) The greater the voltage, the greater the current.

(b.) The greater the current, the greater the voltage.

c. The greater the voltage, the less the current.

d. The greater the current, the less the voltage.

21. If you double the resistance of a conductor, what happens to the

current? _____It is cut in half._____

22. Why are resistors sometimes added to circuits? _____Resistors are added to

prevent too much current from flowing._____

· ·

© Prentice-Hall, Inc.

SECTION 12-3 Series and Parallel Circuits (pages 386–389)

This section describes the parts of an electric circuit and identifies two types of circuits.

▶ Series Circuits (page 387)

1. If all the parts of an electric circuit are connected one after another, the

circuit is called a(n) _____series circuit_____ .

Science Explorer *Focus on Physical Science*

2. In a series circuit, how many paths are there for a current to take?

_____ one _____

3. Suppose you have a number of light bulbs connected together in a series circuit. What happens if one of the bulbs burns out? ____ The burned out ____ bulb acts as a break in the circuit, and none of the other bulbs will light.

4. As more light bulbs are added to a series circuit, the bulbs become dimmer. Why? ____ Adding more bulbs increases the resistance, and as ____ resistance increases, current decreases. The result of less current is that the bulbs burn less brightly.

5. If you wanted to measure the current through some device in a circuit, how would you connect an ammeter? ____ You would connect it in series with ____ the device.

▶ Parallel Circuits (pages 387–388)

6. If different parts of a circuit are on separate branches, the circuit is called a(n) _____ parallel circuit _____.

7. Suppose you have a number of light bulbs connected on a circuit, with each bulb on a separate branch. What happens if one of the bulbs burns out? The other bulbs will remain lit because the current can still move through the other branches.

8. Circle the letter of each sentence that is true about what happens when more branches are added to a parallel circuit.

   a. Resistance increases.   **b.** The current has more paths to follow.

   c. Resistance decreases.   **d.** The current has fewer paths to follow.

CHAPTER 12, Electric Charges and Current *(continued)*

9. Is the following sentence true or false? Adding more paths to a parallel circuit will increase the current. _____ true _____

10. Identify each of the circuits shown here by writing the type of circuit on the line.

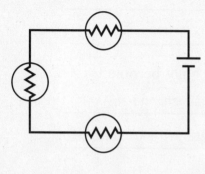

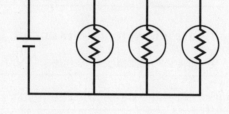

Series circuit   Parallel circuit

▶ **Household Circuits** (page 389)

11. Why wouldn't you want the circuits in your home to be series circuits?
    With a series circuit, all the electrical devices in the home would go off every
    time a light bulb burned out.

12. What kind of circuit carries current to wall sockets and appliances in a home? _____ parallel circuits _____

13. The voltage in household circuits is _____ 120 volts _____.

. . . .

SECTION 12-4 **Electrical Safety** (pages 390–394)

This section describes safety devices used to protect people from the dangers of electricity. It also identifies important rules to follow when using electricity.

▶ **Becoming Part of a Circuit** (pages 390–391)

1. What is a short circuit? _____ A short circuit is a connection that allows current
   to take an unintended path.

© Prentice-Hall, Inc.

Science Explorer Focus on Physical Science

2. If you touch your hand to a 120-volt circuit, a potential difference is

created between your hand and _____Earth_____.

3. Why is it dangerous when the insulation wears off of a wire? __If the___

insulation is gone, the wire is exposed. If a person touches the wire, the

person becomes part of the circuit and is shocked.

▶ **Grounding** (pages 391–392)

4. The round prong of a plug that connects the metal shell of an appliance

to the ground wire of a building is called the _____third prong_____.

5. Circle the letter of the sentence that explains what it means when a
circuit is electrically grounded.

   a. Charges always flow from the intended path to the unintended path.

   b. Short circuits move through the ground instead of through water.

   c. Resistance increases throughout a parallel circuit in the event of a
   short circuit.

   (d.) Charges are able to flow directly from the circuit into the ground
   connection in the event of a short circuit.

6. What is a lightning rod? __It is a metal rod mounted on the roof of a building_

in order to protect a building.

7. When lightning hits a lightning rod, what is the path of the current that

results? __Charges flow through the rod, into a grounding wire, and then into_

Earth.

8. If you are outside during a thunderstorm, would it be safe to hold an

umbrella with a pointed rod through the top? Explain. __It would not be__

safe because lightning would be attracted to the pointed rod. Holding the

umbrella would put you at risk of being hit by lightning.

CHAPTER 12, Electric Charges and Current (continued)

▶ Fuses and Circuit Breakers (pages 392–393)

9. Electric current can become too high if a circuit is overloaded. What might happen if a circuit is overloaded? _Overloading a circuit might result in a fire._

10. In order to prevent circuits from overheating, what are added to circuits? _Devices called fuses and circuit breakers are added to circuits to prevent overheating._

11. Complete the table about fuses and circuit breakers.

Fuses and Circuit Breakers		
Device	**What Happens When Overloaded**	**To Restore Electricity to Circuit**
Fuse	Metal strip melts.	Replace the fuse.
Circuit breaker	Electromagnet shuts off circuit.	Pull back a switch.

▶ Electric Shocks (pages 393–394)

12. Why might an electric shock affect your heart? _Tiny electrical pulses control the beating of the heart. If you receive an electric current from outside the body, the current will interfere with normal processes._

13. Circle the letter of each of the following that you should *never* do.

    a. Use a wire with good insulation on it.

    (b.) Turn on a radio when you're standing in water.

    (c.) Try to repair a toaster while it's still plugged in.

    d. Handle a plug with a third prong on it.

WordWise

Match each definition in the left with the correct term in the right column. Then write the number of each term in the appropriate box below. When you have filled in all the boxes, add up the numbers in each column, row, and two diagonals. All the sums should be the same.

A. The movement of electrons to one part of an object by the electric field of another object

B. A device that contains a thin strip of metal that will melt if too much current flows through it

C. The difference in electrical potential between two places

D. The transfer of electrons from a charged object to another object by direct contact

E. An electric circuit with only one path for current to take

F. A device that measures current

G. The transfer of electrons from one object to another by rubbing

H. An electric circuit with several paths for current to take

I. A device that measures potential difference

1. fuse
2. friction
3. ammeter
4. voltmeter
5. series circuit
6. induction
7. conduction
8. voltage
9. parallel circuit

A	B	C
6	1	8
D	E	F
7	5	3
G	H	I
2	9	4

= 15

= 15

= 15

= 15

= 15

= 15   = 15   = 15

CHAPTER 12, Electric Charges and Current *(continued)*

MathWise

For the problems below, show your calculations. If you need more space, use another sheet of paper. Write the answers for the problems on the lines below.

▶ **Ohm's Law** (pages 382–383)

1. $R = \dfrac{14\ V}{0.2\ A} =$ _____70 Ω_____

2. In a circuit, 15 A is flowing through an electrical appliance. The voltage across the device is 45 V. What is the resistance of the appliance?

   $R = \dfrac{45\ V}{15\ A} = 3\ \Omega$

   Answer: _____R = 3 Ω_____

3. $I = \dfrac{12\ V}{30\ \Omega} =$ _____0.4 A_____

4. The voltage across a light bulb is 6.0 V. The bulb's resistance is 15 Ω. What must the current through the bulb be?

   $I = \dfrac{6.0\ V}{15\ \Omega} = 0.40\ A$

   Answer: _____I = 0.40 A_____

5. $V = 0.60\ A \times 20\ \Omega =$ _____12 V_____

6. For an electrical appliance to work well, a current of 0.80 A must flow through its circuits. If the resistance is 25 Ω, what must the voltage be?

   $V = 0.80\ A \times 25\ \Omega = 20\ V$

   Answer: _____V = 20 V_____

Science Explorer *Focus on Physical Science*

CHAPTER 13

ELECTRICITY AND MAGNETISM AT WORK

SECTION 13-1 **Electricity, Magnetism, and Motion** (pages 400-403)

This section explains how electrical energy can be converted to mechanical energy. It also describes how an electric motor works.

▶ Electrical and Mechanical Energy (pages 400–401)

1. The ability to move an object some distance is called ___energy___.

2. Complete the table about forms of energy.

Forms of Energy	
Energy Form	**Definition**
Electrical energy	The energy associated with electric currents
Mechanical energy	The energy an object has due to its movement or position

3. When a current-carrying wire is placed in a magnetic field, what energy conversion occurs? ___Electrical energy is converted into mechanical energy.___ _____

▶ Galvanometers (pages 401–402)

4. A device that uses an electromagnet to measure small amounts of current is called a(n) ___galvanometer___.

5. What is used to turn the pointer of a galvanometer?
   ___electric current___

CHAPTER 13, Electricity and Magnetism at Work *(continued)*

6. In a galvanometer, what does the amount of rotation of the loops of

   wire and the pointer depend on? It depends on the amount of current in

   the wire.

▶ Electric Motors (pages 402–403)

7. A device that uses an electric current to turn an axle is called a(n)

   _____electric motor_____.

8. What energy conversion occurs in an electric motor? An electric motor

   converts electrical energy into mechanical energy.

9. A device that reverses the flow of current through an electric motor is

   called a(n) _____commutator_____.

10. What does a commutator consist of? It consists of two parts of a ring.

   _____

11. As a commutator moves, it slides past two contact points called

   _____brushes_____.

12. The arrangement of wires wrapped around an iron core in an electric

   motor is called a(n) _____armature_____.

. . . .

SECTION 13-2 Generating Electric Current (pages 406-413)

This section explains the production of electric current. It also describes electric generators.

▶ Induction of Electric Current (pages 406–407)

1. The current that results from electromagnetic induction is called a(n)

   _____induced current_____.

© Prentice-Hall, Inc.

2. When will an electric current be produced in a conductor? __An electric__ current will be produced when the conductor moves across the lines of a magnetic field.

3. What are two cases in which an electric current can be produced with a conductor and a magnet?

a. The conductor can move through the magnetic field.

b. The magnet itself can move through the conductor.

4. What is electromagnetic induction? It is the process of generating an electric current from the motion of a conductor through a magnetic field.

▶ Alternating and Direct Current (pages 407–408)

5. What does the direction of an induced current depend on? The direction depends on the direction in which the wire or magnet moves.

6. Is the following sentence true or false? The flow of an induced current may change direction. ____true____

7. Complete the table about induced currents.

Induced Currents			
Induced Current	**Abbreviation**	**Description**	**Example**
Alternating current	AC	A current consisting of charges that move back and forth in a circuit	Circuits in the home
Direct current	DC	A current consisting of charges that flow in one direction only	Batteries

CHAPTER 13, Electricity and Magnetism at Work *(continued)*

▶ Generators (pages 408–409)

8. A device that converts mechanical energy into electrical energy is called

a(n) _____electric generator_____.

9. How is an electric motor the opposite of an electric generator? __An__

electric motor uses an electric current to produce motion. An electric

generator uses motion to produce an electric current.

10. Is the following sentence true or false? Large generators use armatures

similar to those in a motor. _____true_____

11. The parts of a generator that rotate with the wire loop and make

contact with the brushes are called _____slip rings_____.

▶ Turbines (pages 409–411)

12. Complete the table about energy resources. See *Exploring Energy
Resources* on pages 410–411.

Energy Resources		
Resource	**Source of Energy**	**What Turns a Turbine**
Nuclear energy	Energy in atom's nucleus	Steam
Hydroelectricity	Falling water	Moving water
Solar energy	Sun's rays	Steam
Tidal energy	Movement of tides	Moving water
Geothermal energy	Heated underground water	Steam
Energy from wind	Wind	Windmill
Energy from fossil fuels	Chemical energy in fossil fuels	Steam

13. A circular device made up of many blades that is turned by water, wind, steam, or tides is called a(n) _____turbine_____.

▶ Generating Electricity (pages 412–413)

14. According to the graph in Figure 9 on page 412, what is the leading resource for generating electricity in the United States?

_____coal_____

15. What percentage of electricity does nuclear energy generate?

_____21.9%_____

16. Is the following sentence true or false? Cost is a very important factor in the generation of electricity. _____true_____

17. According to Figure 10 on page 412, what are the pros of using coal?

The pros are moderate cost and a large supply.

18. What are three cons of using coal to produce electricity?

a. Large deposits are localized.

b. Mining damages land and water and is hazardous to miners.

c. Burning coal produces air pollution.

19. Which energy resources have pros of "no wastes"? Hydroelectricity, sun, and tides

20. Complete the table about energy resources.

Energy Resources		
Type of Resource	**Definition**	**Examples**
Renewable resource	A resource that can be replaced in nature at a rate close to the rate at which it is used	Wind energy, tidal energy, geothermal energy, solar energy
Nonrenewable resource	A resource that exists in a fixed amount	Fossil fuels such as coal, oil, and natural gas

CHAPTER 13, Electricity and Magnetism at Work *(continued)*

 Reading Skill Practice

A graph can help you understand comparisons of data at a glance. Use a piece of graph paper to convert the circle graph in Figure 9 on page 412 into a bar graph. On the graph paper, draw a vertical, or *y*-, axis. The bottom of that line should be labeled 0. The top of the line should be labeled 100%. Then draw a horizontal, or *x*-, axis. Along that line write the names of the energy resources shown in the circle graph. For each resource, draw a solid bar that represents its percentage. For more information about bar graphs, see page 834 in the Skills Handbook of your textbook.

Students' bar graphs should have six bars with percentages that correspond to those in the Energy Resources circle graph on page 412.

SECTION 13-3 **Using Electric Power**
(pages 414–420)

This section explains how you can calculate power and energy use. It also explains how voltage can be increased or decreased.

▶ Electric Power (page 415)

1. What is power? __Power is the rate at which energy is converted from one__

   __form into another.__

2. The power used by a light bulb or an appliance depends on what two factors?

   a. __voltage__   b. __current__

3. What formula do you use to calculate power?

   __Power = Voltage × Current, or Watts = Volts × Amps__

4. Use Figure 13 on page 415 to rank the following appliances according to how much power they use. Rank the appliance with the highest power rating as *1*.

   __5__ a. toaster   __4__ b. microwave oven

   __2__ c. clothes dryer   __3__ d. water heater

   __6__ e. color television   __1__ f. stove

▶ Paying for Energy (page 416)

5. What two factors does the energy use on an electric bill depend on?

a. <u>power</u>

b. <u>time</u>

6. What formula do you use to determine the amount of energy used by an appliance?

<u>Energy = Power × Time, or E = P × T</u>

7. Electric power is usually measured in thousands of watts, or <u>kilowatts (kW)</u>.

8. The unit of electrical energy is the <u>kilowatt-hour (kWh)</u>.

9. What is the specific energy equation you would use to determine the amount of electrical energy used by an appliance?

<u>Kilowatt-hours = Kilowatts × Hours</u>

▶ Transformers (pages 416–417)

10. A device that increases or decreases voltage is called a(n) <u>transformer</u>.

11. Why is a transformer necessary so that electricity can be brought into a home? <u>The most efficient way to transmit current over long distances is to maintain very high voltages. But electricity is used at much lower voltages in the home, and a transformer can decrease the voltage.</u>

12. In a transformer, what induces a current in the secondary coil? <u>The AC current flowing through the primary coil creates a changing magnetic field, which induces a current in the secondary coil.</u>

CHAPTER 13, Electricity and Magnetism at Work *(continued)*

13. Why won't a transformer work with direct current? __A transformer__

works only if the current in the primary coil is changing. In direct current, the

current does not change, and thus, the magnetic field does not change.

▶ **Changing Voltage** (pages 417–418)

14. If there are more loops in the secondary coil of a transformer than in the primary coil, will the voltage in the secondary coil be higher or

lower than in the primary coil? __The voltage will be higher.__

15. Complete the table below about types of transformers.

Types of Transformers		
Type of Transformer	**Increases or Decreases Voltage?**	**Setup**
Step-down transformer	Decreases	Soft iron core / Alternating current source / Secondary coil / Primary coil
Step-up transformer	Increases	Soft iron core / Alternating current source / Secondary coil / Primary coil

▶ **The War of the Currents** (pages 418–420)

16. Why did Nikola Tesla think AC would be better for distribution of

electricity to homes? __He thought distributing AC current to homes would__

be safer and more efficient than distributing DC current.

Science Explorer Focus on Physical Science

17. What does using alternating current with transformers reduce in long

transmission wires? _____ energy losses _____

18. In Figure 17 on page 420, what hangs on the telephone pole just

outside the house? What is the purpose of that device? __A step-down__

transformer hangs on the pole. Its purpose is to decrease the voltage from

2,400 volts to 120 volts for use by household appliances.

_____

SECTION 13-4 **Batteries** (pages 421-425)

This section explains how chemical reactions can generate electricity. It also describes how some batteries can be recharged.

▶ The First Battery (pages 422–423)

1. The energy stored in chemical compounds is called

_____ chemical energy _____.

2. What is a chemical reaction? __A chemical reaction is a process in which__

substances change into new substances with different properties.

_____

3. In the year 1800, who designed the first electric battery?

_____ Alessandro Volta _____

4. In Volta's battery, a chemical reaction between which two metals

produced a current? _____ silver and zinc _____

▶ Electrochemical Cells (pages 423–424)

5. A device that converts chemical energy into electrical energy is called

a(n) _____ electrochemical cell _____.

CHAPTER 13, Electricity and Magnetism at Work *(continued)*

Match the term with its description.

Term	Definition
_b_ **6.** electrode	**a.** The part used to connect the cell to a circuit
_c_ **7.** electrolyte	**b.** A metal in an electrochemical cell
_a_ **8.** terminal	**c.** A substance that conducts electric current

9. What occurs between the electrodes and the electrolyte in an

electrochemical cell? _____ Chemical reactions occur. _____

10. How do the chemical reactions change the electrodes? ___ One electrode ___

becomes negatively charged, and the other becomes positively charged.

▶ Dead and Rechargeable Batteries *(page 425)*

11. A combination of two or more electrochemical cells in a series is called

a(n) _____ battery _____.

12. Is the following sentence true or false? The voltage of a battery is the

sum of the voltages of the cells. _____ true _____

13. Two or more electrochemical cells are connected in a(n)

_____ series _____.

14. Complete the table about wet and dry cells.

Electrochemical Cells		
Type of Cell	**Electrolyte—Liquid or Dry?**	**Example**
Wet cell	Liquid	Auto battery
Dry cell	Dry	Flashlight battery

15. A battery in which the products of the electrochemical reaction can be

turned back into reactants to be reused is called a(n)

_____ rechargeable battery _____.

WordWise

Solve the clues by filling in the blanks with key terms from Chapter 13. Then write the numbered letters in the correct order to find the hidden message.

Clues	Key Terms
An electrochemical cell in which the electrolyte is a liquid	w e t c e l l 1
The arrangement of wires wrapped around an iron core in an electric motor	a r m a t u r e 2
A substance that conducts electric current	e l e c t r o l y t e 3
A current consisting of charges that flow in one direction only	d i r e c t c u r r e n t 4
A device that increases or decreases voltage	t r a n s f o r m e r 5
A device that uses an electromagnet to measure small amounts of current	g a l v a n o m e t e r 6
A metal in an electrochemical cell	e l e c t r o d e 7
An electrochemical cell in which the electrolyte is a paste	d r y c e l l 8
A transformer that decreases voltage	s t e p – d o w n 9
The contact points connected to a commutator of an electric motor	b r u s h e s 10
A combination of two or more electrochemical cells in a series	b a t t e r y 11
A device that reverses the flow of current through an electric motor	c o m m u t a t o r 12
The rate at which energy is converted from one form into another	p o w e r 13
The parts of a generator that rotate with the wire loop and make contact with the brushes	s l i p r i n g s 14

Hidden Message

$$\underset{1}{w}\ \underset{2}{a}\ \underset{3}{t}\ \underset{4}{t}\ \underset{5}{s}\ =\ \underset{6}{v}\ \underset{7}{o}\ \underset{8}{l}\ \underset{9}{t}\ \underset{10}{s}\ \times\ \underset{11}{a}\ \underset{12}{m}\ \underset{13}{p}\ \underset{14}{s}$$

CHAPTER 13, Electricity and Magnetism at Work (continued)

MathWise

For the problems below, show your calculations. If you need more space, use another sheet of paper. Write the answers for the problems on the lines below.

▶ Calculating Power (page 415)

1. Power = 120 volts × 4 amps = _____ 480 watts

2. A boombox uses six 1.5-volt batteries in series to create a current of 0.4 amps. What is the power rating of the radio?

   P = 9 volts × 0.4 amps = 3.6 watts

   Answer: _____ Power = 3.6 watts

3. Current = $\dfrac{60 \text{ watts}}{120 \text{ volts}}$ = _____ 0.5 amps

4. A guitar amplifier has a power rating of 180 watts and uses a standard voltage of 120 volts. What is the current through the guitar amplifier?

   I = $\dfrac{180 \text{ watts}}{120 \text{ volts}}$ = 1.5 amps

   Answer: _____ Current = 1.5 amps

▶ Calculating Electrical Energy (page 416)

5. Electrical energy = 4 kilowatts × 6 hours = _____ 24 kilowatt-hours

6. You dry four pairs of jeans in a clothes dryer for 2 hours. A clothes dryer has a power rating of 5,400 watts. How much electrical energy did you use to dry your jeans?

   Electrical energy = 5,400 watts × 2 hours = 5.4 kilowatts × 2 hours = 10.8 kilowatt-hours

   Answer: _____ Electrical energy = 10.8 kilowatt-hours

CHAPTER 14

AN INTRODUCTION TO MATTER

• •

SECTION 14-1 **Describing Matter**
(pages 438-445)

This section describes the three states of matter and the characteristic properties of matter. It also explains how matter can be classified.

▶ Properties of Matter (pages 438–439)

1. Is the following sentence true or false? Matter can be of any shape, any texture, and any color. _____true_____

2. What are the three principal states of matter?

   a. __solids_____ b. __liquids_____ c. __gases_____

▶ Characteristic Properties (pages 439–440)

3. What are characteristic properties of matter? __They are properties that__ hold true for a particular kind of substance no matter what the sample. _____

   _____

4. Circle the letter of the reason why characteristic properties can be used to identify unknown substances.

   a. For a given substance they never change.

   b. Some properties are true only for a given sample of matter.

   c. For a given substance no properties hold true.

   d. There are only three principal states of matter.

5. The temperature at which a liquid boils is called its

   _____boiling point_____ .

CHAPTER 14, An Introduction to Matter (continued)

6. Water, chloroform, and ethanol are all clear, colorless liquids. What could you do to identify an unknown liquid as one of these three?

You could determine the boiling point of the unknown liquid, because each

of these liquids boils at a different temperature.

7. The temperature at which a solid melts is called its

_____melting point_____.

8. Why must you study at least two or three characteristic properties before you can accurately identify a substance? __Many substances share__

melting points, boiling points, or other characteristic properties.

9. Is the following sentence true or false? Neither boiling point nor melting point can be considered characteristic properties of matter.

_____false_____

▶ Changes in Matter (page 441)

10. What are physical changes? __They are changes that alter the form of a__

substance, but not its identity.

11. What are chemical changes? __They are changes in which one or more__

substances combine or decompose to form new substances.

12. The ability to undergo a chemical change is a characteristic property

called the _____chemical activity_____ of a substance.

13. Complete the table by classifying each change as either a physical change or a chemical change.

Changes in Matter	
Change	**Physical or Chemical Change?**
Wood burns	Chemical
Soda can is crushed	Physical
Orange juice is filtered	Physical
Sugar is changed into caramel	Chemical
Water boils away	Physical

▶ Types of Matter (page 442)

14. Complete the concept map about types of matter.

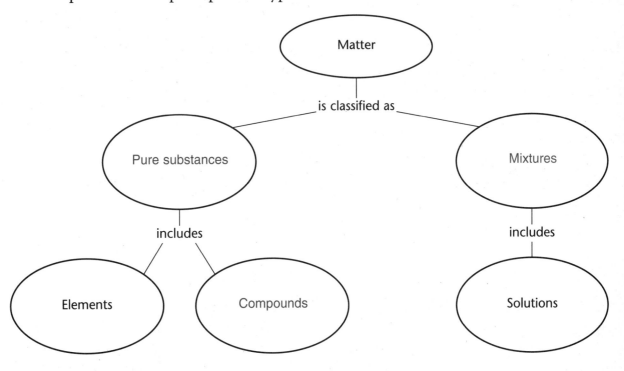

▶ Mixtures (page 442)

15. What does a mixture consist of? __A mixture consists of two or more__
__substances that are mixed together but not chemically combined.__

_____

© Prentice-Hall, Inc.

CHAPTER 14, An Introduction to Matter *(continued)*

16. When substances are in a mixture, what does each substance keep?

Each keeps its individual properties.

17. The "best-mixed" of all mixtures is called a(n) _____solution_____.

18. What are two examples of a solution?

a. sea water   b. sugar water

▶ Pure Substances (pages 443–445)

19. A substance made of only one kind of matter and having definite

properties is called a(n) _____pure substance_____.

20. Is the following sentence true or false? Water is not a pure substance
because it changes every time it's mixed with something else.

_____false_____

21. Pure substances that cannot be broken down into other substances by

any chemical means are called _____elements_____.

22. How many elements are there? _____There are a little more than 100 different_____

elements.

23. What is a compound? _____A compound is a pure substance formed from_____

chemical combinations of two or more different elements.

▶ Matter Is All Around You (page 445)

24. Consider the chair you're sitting in. What state is it in? Is it a pure
substance or a mixture? Can you identify any elements in the chair?

Answers may vary depending on the types of chairs. All chairs are in a solid

state, and almost all chairs are mixtures. Students might be able to identify

a metallic element in a chair, such as aluminum or iron.

● ●

SECTION 14-2 Measuring Matter (pages 446-451)

This section explains the difference between mass and weight. It also explains what the density of a substance is.

▶ Mass (pages 446–447)

1. A measure of the force of gravity on an object is called _____weight_____.

2. Why would you weigh less on the moon than you do on Earth? __The__ force of gravity is much less on the moon than it is on Earth. _____

3. What is mass? __Mass is a measurement of how much matter an object__ contains. _____

4. Why do scientists rely on mass rather than weight as the measurement of how much matter an object contains? __Mass is constant wherever an__ object may be, while weight changes. _____

5. What system of units do scientists use to measure the properties of matter? They use the International System of Units. _____

6. The SI unit for mass is _____kilogram_____.

▶ Volume (pages 447–449)

7. The amount of space that matter occupies is called its _____volume_____.

8. What formula do you use to find the volume of a rectangular object? Volume = Length × Width × Height _____

9. What are the SI/metric units for volume listed in Figure 9 on page 450?

  a. __cubic meter (m³)__   b. __liter (L)__

  c. __milliliter (mL)__   d. __cubic centimeter (cm³)__

CHAPTER 14, An Introduction to Matter *(continued)*

▶ Density (pages 450–451)

10. What is density? Density is the measurement of how much mass is

contained in a given volume.

11. Why does a kilogram of bricks take up a much smaller space than a

kilogram of feathers? Bricks and feathers have different densities.

_____

12. What formula do you use to calculate the density of an object?

Density = $\dfrac{\text{Mass}}{\text{Volume}}$

13. One unit of density is g/cm³. How do you say that unit in words?

Grams per cubic centimeter

14. What unit of measurement is used for the density of liquids?

Grams per milliliter, or g/mL

15. If you drop a block of gold and a block of wood into water, the gold
sinks and the wood floats. What can you conclude about the density of

gold and wood compared to the density of water? Water has a density

of 1.0 g/cm³. Since wood floats, its density must be less than 1.0 g/cm³.

Since gold sinks, its density must be greater than 1.0 g/cm³.

16. Is the following sentence true or false? The density of a substance varies

with the samples of that substance. _____ false _____

 ## Reading Skill Practice

Outlining is a way to help yourself understand and remember what you have read. Write an
outline of Section 14–2, Measuring Matter. In your outline, copy the headings in the textbook.
Under each heading, write the main idea. Then list the details that support, or back up, the main
idea. Do your work on a separate sheet of paper.

The major heads of students' outlines of the section should be *Mass, Volume,* and *Density*. The
section's subheads should form the next level of the outline.

● ●

SECTION 14-3 **Particles of Matter** (pages 453-457)

This section explains what atoms are and describes how scientists model atoms today.

▶ Atoms (page 454)

1. The smallest particles of an element are called ___atoms___.

▶ Democritus (page 454)

2. Who was Democritus? ___Democritus was a Greek philosopher.___

3. Why did Democritus call the smallest piece of matter *atomos*? ___That is___ the Greek word for "uncuttable."

▶ Dalton's Ideas (page 455)

4. Who was John Dalton? ___He was a British school teacher in the early___ 1800s.

5. Complete the table about characteristics of atoms.

Atoms	
Characteristic	**Result**
Atoms can't be broken down into ___smaller pieces___ .	Atoms are nearly impossible to break apart.
In any element, all atoms are ___exactly alike___ .	An element always has the same properties.
Atoms of two or more elements can combine to form ___compounds___ .	Compounds break down into elements.
Atoms of each element have a unique ___mass___ .	The atoms of any element have an identifiable mass.
The masses of elements in a compound are always in a(n) ___constant ratio___ .	In any sample of a compound, the ratio of the masses of elements is always the same.

CHAPTER 14, An Introduction to Matter *(continued)*

▶ Atoms and Molecules Today (pages 456–457)

6. Circle the letter of the term that means a group of atoms that are joined together and act as a single unit.

   a. atom

   b. solution

   (**c.**) molecule

   d. particle

7. What is the force that holds two atoms together?

   _____chemical bond_____

8. Is the following sentence true or false? Molecules can contain as many as a billion atoms. _____true_____

9. With what tool did scientists capture the image of silicon atoms, as shown in Figure 15 on page 457? _____scanning tunneling microscope_____

10. When you think about matter in terms of atoms and molecules, you are using a model known as the _____particle model of matter_____.

· ·

SECTION 14-4 Elements From Earth (pages 458-462)

This section explains how the density of gold allows it to be separated from other substances. It also describes how copper and iron can be separated from rocks that contain them.

▶ Gold and Density (page 459)

1. Why can density be used to separate gold from surrounding material?

   Gold is much denser than the sand and dirt with which it is mixed, and it is

   also much denser than its look-alike, pyrite.

   _____

Science Explorer *Focus on Physical Science*

2. What is gold's density compared to pyrite? Gold's density is 19.3 g/cm³, while pyrite's density is only 5.0 g/cm³.

3. Today, gold mining is done with big machines called _____dredges_____.

▶ Copper and Electrolysis (pages 459–461)

4. How is copper most often found in nature? Copper most often exists as a compound with some other element.

5. What is an ore? An ore is a rock that contains a metal or some other economically useful element.

6. What characteristic property of copper is used to extract it from copper ore? Its chemical activity is used.

7. A process by which an electric current breaks a chemical bond is called _____electrolysis_____.

8. Complete the flowchart about the electrolysis of an ore.

Copper Electrolysis

A battery produces a(n) _____electric current_____.

↓

The current flows through wire to _____electrodes_____, which are in a solution made of the _____ore_____.

↓

One electrode attracts the _____metal_____ of the ore, while the other attracts other components.

↓

The _____metal_____ is scraped off and used.

CHAPTER 14, An Introduction to Matter *(continued)*

▶ Iron and Chemical Activity (page 462)

9. What materials are placed into a hot fire to release iron? __Iron-containing__

   ores and carbon are placed into a hot fire.

   _____

10. Where does the carbon that is used to purify iron come from? __It__

    comes from a material called coke, which is made from coal.

    _____

    _____

11. What characteristic property of both iron and carbon is utilized to

    purify iron metal? __chemical activity__

12. Complete the flowchart about how purified iron is produced.

Miners mine iron _____ore_____, or rocks that contain iron
chemically combined with other elements.

⬇

Chunks of iron ore and a material called _____coke_____ are
placed in a(n) _____blast_____ furnace.

⬇

At very high temperatures, the _____carbon_____ in the coke reacts
with the _____oxygen_____ in the iron ore.

⬇

The result of the chemical reactions in the blast furnace is purified
_____iron_____ .

⬇

The purified iron is then mixed with other elements to make
_____steel_____ .

© Prentice-Hall, Inc.

WordWise

Complete the following paragraphs using the list of words and phrases below. Each word or phrase may be used only once.

Word Bank

atoms	boiling point	density	molecule	elements	weight
mixture	melting point	mass	chemical bond	compound	solution
pure substance	chemical properties		volume	chemical activity	

Some properties of matter, such as size or amount, are true only for a given sample of matter. But ___characteristic properties___ hold true for a particular kind of substance no matter what the sample. One characteristic property is the temperature at which a liquid boils, called the ___boiling point___. Another is the temperature at which a solid melts, called the ___melting point___. A third characteristic property is ___chemical activity___, a substance's ability to undergo chemical change.

Matter can be classified into mixtures and pure substances. A(n) ___mixture___ consists of two or more substances that are mixed together but not chemically combined. The "best-mixed" of all possible mixtures is called a(n) ___solution___. A(n) ___pure substance___ is made of only one kind of matter and has definite properties. Some pure substances, called ___elements___, cannot be broken down into other substances by any chemical means. A pure substance formed from chemical combinations of two or more elements is a(n) ___compound___.

The smallest particles of elements are called ___atoms___. Atoms can combine to form different compounds. A group of atoms that are joined together and act as a single unit is a(n) ___molecule___. The force that holds two atoms together is called a(n) ___chemical bond___.

There are all sorts of ways of measuring matter. The measurement of the force of gravity on an object is ___weight___. The measurement of how much matter an object contains is ___mass___. The measurement of the amount of space that matter occupies is ___volume___. The measurement of how much mass is contained in a given volume is ___density___.

CHAPTER 14, An Introduction to Matter *(continued)*

MathWise

For the problems below, show your calculations. If you need more space, use another sheet of paper. Write the answers for the problems on the lines below.

▶ Calculating Volume of a Rectangular Object (page 448)

1. Volume = 10 cm × 5 cm × 6 cm = _____300 cm³_____

2. A box has a length of 25 centimeters, a width of 8 centimeters, and a height of 12 centimeters. What is its volume?

   Volume = 25 cm × 8 cm × 12 cm = 2,400 cm³

   Answer: _____Volume = 2,400 cm³_____

▶ Calculating Density (pages 450–451)

3. Density = $\dfrac{24 \text{ g}}{8 \text{ cm}^3}$ = _____3 g/cm³_____

4. A sample of water has a mass of 13 grams and a volume of 13 milliliters. What is the density of water?

   Density = $\dfrac{13 \text{ g}}{13 \text{ mL}}$ = 1 g/mL

   Answer: _____Density = 1 g/mL_____

5. A sample of metal has a mass of 94.5 grams and a volume of 7 cubic centimeters. What is its density?

   Density = $\dfrac{94.5 \text{ g}}{7 \text{ cm}^3}$ = 13.5 g/cm³

   Answer: _____Density = 13.5 g/cm³_____

6. A sample of liquid has a mass of 26 grams and a volume of 20 milliliters. What is its density?

   Density = $\dfrac{26 \text{ g}}{20 \text{ mL}}$ = 1.3 g/mL

   Answer: _____Density = 1.3 g/mL_____

CHAPTER 15

CHANGES IN MATTER

• •

SECTION 15–1 **Solids, Liquids, and Gases** (pages 468–472)

This section explains how shape, volume, and the motion of particles are useful in describing solids, liquids, and gases.

▶ **Solids** (pages 469–470)

1. Which state of matter has a definite volume and a definite shape?

   _____solid_____

2. Is the following sentence true or false? A solid will keep its volume and

   its shape in any position and in any container. _____true_____

3. Why do solids have a definite shape and a definite volume? ____The____

   particles in a solid are packed tightly together and stay in fixed positions.

   _____

   _____

4. Complete the table about types of solids.

Solids			
Type of Solid	**Description**	**Examples**	**Melting Point**
Crystalline solids	Made up of crystals	Salt, sugar, sand, snow	Distinct melting point
Amorphous solids	Particles not arranged in a regular pattern	Plastics, rubber, glass	No distinct melting point

© Prentice-Hall, Inc.

CHAPTER 15, Changes in Matter *(continued)*

5. Circle the letter of each sentence that is true about particles in a solid.

   a. They are completely motionless.

   (b.) They stay in about the same position.

   (c.) They vibrate back and forth.

   d. They switch positions occasionally.

▶ Liquids (pages 470–471)

6. Which state of matter has no definite shape but does have a definite volume? _____liquid_____

7. Is the following sentence true or false? A liquid's volume does not change no matter the shape of the container. _____true_____

8. A substance that flows is called a(n) _____fluid_____.

9. Circle the letter of the term that means the resistance of a liquid to flowing.

   a. amorphous

   b. solid

   (c.) viscosity

   d. insulator

10. Is the following sentence true or false? Liquids with high viscosity flow quickly. _____false_____

▶ Gases (pages 471–472)

11. Which state of matter has neither definite shape nor volume?

    _____gas_____

12. If you put a gas into a container with a top, what will the gas do? __It will__ spread apart or squeeze together to fill that container. _____

    _____

13. The volume and shape of a gas are determined by its _____container_____.

14. In the containers below, draw how the particles are arranged in the three states of matter.

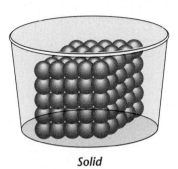

Solid

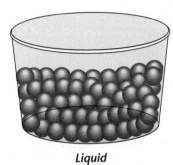

Liquid

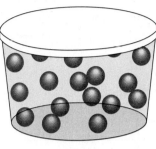

Gas

SECTION 15-2 Behavior of Gases (pages 473-479)

This section explains how the volume, temperature, and pressure of a gas are related.

▶ Measuring Gases (pages 474–475)

1. The volume of a gas is the same as the volume of its _____ container _____.

2. What is temperature? _____ Temperature is a measure of the average energy

of motion of the particles of a substance. _____

3. The force exerted on a surface divided by the total area over which the

force is exerted is called _____ pressure _____.

4. What is the formula you use to calculate pressure?

$$Pressure = \frac{Force}{Area}$$

▶ Relating Pressure and Volume (pages 475–476)

5. What does Boyle's law say about the relationship between the pressure

and volume of a gas? _____ When the pressure of a gas increases, its volume

decreases. When the pressure of a gas decreases, its volume increases. _____

CHAPTER 15, Changes in Matter *(continued)*

6. Complete the table about the relationship between the pressure and volume of a gas.

Pressure and Volume of Gases	
Change	**Increases or Decreases?**
Pressure decreases	Volume increases
Pressure increases	Volume decreases
Volume increases	Pressure decreases
Volume decreases	Pressure increases

▶ Relating Pressure and Temperature (pages 476–477)

7. Suppose a gas is kept in a closed, rigid container. If the temperature of the gas increases, what happens to its pressure on the container?
The pressure increases.
_____

8. If the temperature of that gas in the container decreases, what happens to its pressure? __The pressure decreases.__
_____

9. How is pressure affected by the collisions of gas particles? __The more__ collisions there are, the greater the pressure will be.

▶ Volume and Temperature (pages 478–479)

10. What is Charles's law? __When the temperature of a gas is increased at__ constant pressure, its volume increases.
_____

11. Is the following sentence true or false? At higher temperatures, the particles of a gas move slower. _____false_____

© Prentice-Hall, Inc.

12. If the temperature of a gas decreases, what happens to its volume?

Its volume decreases.

13. Why does a basketball left outside on a cold winter night become soft

and lose its bounce? The air inside the basketball is chilled by the cold

winter air. As the temperature of the air decreased, so did its volume.

Therefore, the volume of the air inside the ball decreased, making the ball

soft and less bouncy.

 Reading Skill Practice

By looking carefully at photographs and illustrations in textbooks, you can help yourself better understand what you have read. Look carefully at Figure 12 on page 476. What important idea does this illustration communicate? Do your work on a separate sheet of paper.

The illustration communicates visually the relationship known as Boyle's law. As the pressure of a gas increases, its volume decreases.

• •

SECTION 15–3 Graphing Gas Behavior (pages 480-483)

This section describes graphs for Charles's law and Boyle's law.

▶ Introduction (page 480)

1. What is a graph? A graph is a diagram that shows how two variables are

related.

2. Is the following sentence true or false? Graphs show how changes in one

variable result in changes in a second variable. _____true_____

CHAPTER 15, Changes in Matter *(continued)*

▶ Temperature and Volume (pages 481–482)

3. In the experiment represented in Figure 17 on page 481, what is the

volume of gas when the temperature is 0°C? _____50 mL_____

4. When the temperature of the gas rises to 353 kelvins, what is the

volume of the gas? _____66 mL_____

5. On the graph below, label the *x*-axis and the *y*-axis.

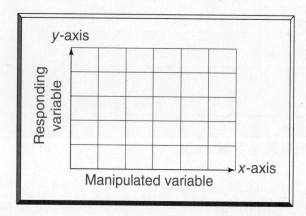

6. Write labels on the graph above that show on which axis the units for the manipulated variable should be placed and on which axis the units for the responding variable should be placed.

7. Where did the data come from that was used to create the graph in

Figure 19 on page 482? __The data came from the experiment shown in__

__Figure 17._____

8. Compare Figure 18 on page 481 with Figure 19 on page 482. On Figure 19,

what is the manipulated variable? __The manipulated variable is the__

__temperature in kelvins of the gas._____

_____

9. What is the responding variable on Figure 19? __The responding variable__

__is the volume in milliliters of the gas._____

_____

10. When a graph of two variables is a straight line passing through the (0,0) point, the relationship is linear and the variables are said to be _____ directly proportional _____ to each other.

11. What does the graph of Charles's law show about the relationship between the temperature and volume of a gas? _____ The graph shows that _____ the volume of a gas is directly proportional to its kelvin temperature under _____ constant pressure. _____

▶ Pressure and Volume (pages 482–483)

12. In the experiment shown in Figure 20 on page 482, what is the volume and pressure of the gas when the experiment begins? _____ The volume is _____ 100 mL and the pressure is 60 kPa. _____

13. In that experiment, does the pressure increase or decrease as the volume decreases? _____ The pressure increases. _____

14. On the graph in Figure 21 on page 483, what is the manipulated variable and what is the responding variable? _____ The manipulated variable _____ is volume in milliliters, and the responding variable is pressure in kilopascals. _____

15. When a graph of two measurements forms a curve that becomes less steep close to the horizontal axis, the relationship is nonlinear and the measurements are said to _____ vary inversely _____ with one another.

16. What does the graph for Boyle's law show about the relationship between the pressure and volume of a gas? _____ The pressure of a gas varies _____ inversely with its volume at constant temperature. _____

CHAPTER 15, Changes in Matter (continued)

SECTION 15-4 **Physical and Chemical Changes**
(pages 486-493)

This section explains how physical and chemical changes differ. It also describes changes of state.

▶ Energy and Change (pages 486–487)

1. Complete the table about change.

Changing Matter		
Type of Change	**Definition**	**Example**
Physical change	Alters the form of a substance, but does not change it to another substance	Tearing a piece of paper, bending a nail, spinning wool
Chemical change	Changes the substance into a different substance with different properties	Burning wood

2. The total energy of a substance's particles due to their movement or vibration is called _____ thermal energy _____.

3. The energy stored within the chemical bonds of chemical compounds is called _____ chemical energy _____.

4. Circle the letter of each sentence that is true about changes in matter.

   (a.) Matter changes whenever energy is added.

   b. Matter changes whenever energy is destroyed.

   (c.) Matter changes whenever energy is taken away.

   d. Matter changes whenever energy is created.

5. What is the principle called that says that in every physical and chemical change the total amount of energy stays the same? The law of _____ conservation of energy

▶ Changes Between Liquid and Solid (page 488)

6. The change in state from a solid to a liquid is called _____melting_____.

7. In most pure substances, melting occurs at a specific temperature called the _____melting point_____.

8. The change of state from liquid to solid is called _____freezing_____.

9. Is the following statement true or false? The energy loss during the freezing of water changes the arrangement of water's molecules. _____true_____

▶ Changes Between Liquid and Gas (pages 489–490)

10. The change from the liquid to the gas state of matter is called _____vaporization_____.

11. Complete the concept map.

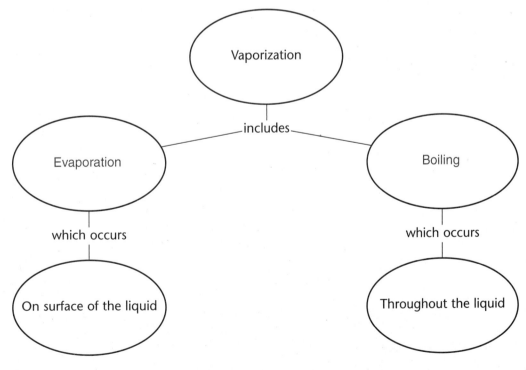

CHAPTER 15, Changes in Matter *(continued)*

12. Each liquid boils only at a certain temperature, which is called its

_____boiling point_____ .

13. Why is the boiling point of water lower in the mountains than it is at

sea level? __Air pressure is lower in the mountains. The lower the air__

__pressure above a liquid, the less energy that liquid molecules need to__

__escape into the air.__

_____

_____

14. The change in state from a gas to a liquid is called ____condensation____ .

15. Is the following sentence true or false? Condensation is the opposite of

vaporization. _____true_____

16. When condensation occurs, does a gas lose or gain thermal energy?

__It loses thermal energy.__

_____

▶ Changes Between Solid and Gas (pages 490–491)

Match the term with its example.

	Term	Example
_b_	**17.** vaporization	**a.** A pot of water on a stove reaches its boiling point.
_d_	**18.** evaporation	**b.** Liquid water changes into water vapor.
_a_	**19.** boiling	**c.** Clouds form from water vapor in the sky.
_c_	**20.** condensation	**d.** A puddle dries up after a rain shower.

21. The change of state from a solid directly to a gas without passing

through the liquid state is called ____sublimation____ .

22. Give an example of sublimation. <u>Snow, a solid, evaporating into water</u>

<u>vapor; dry ice changing into carbon dioxide gas</u>

▶ **Chemical Changes** (pages 492–493)

23. Is the following sentence true or false? Changes in state are examples of

chemical changes. _____<u>false</u>_____

24. A process in which substances undergo chemical changes is called a(n)

_____<u>chemical reaction</u>_____.

25. Circle each sentence that is true about chemical reactions.

(**a.**) All chemical reactions either absorb or release energy.

b. After a chemical change, the substance is the same as the substance
you started with.

(**c.**) In some chemical reactions, two or more substances combine to
form new substances.

(**d.**) All chemical reactions produce new substances.

26. Complete the flowchart about energy and chemical reactions in plants.

```
┌─────────────────────────────────────────────────────────────────┐
│                          light energy                             │
│   Plants capture _____ from the sun.        │
└─────────────────────────────────────────────────────────────────┘
                                 │
                                 ▼
┌─────────────────────────────────────────────────────────────────┐
│                                      chemical energy              │
│   The plants change energy from the sun into _____ in  │
│   the form of various compounds.                                  │
└─────────────────────────────────────────────────────────────────┘
                                 │
                                 ▼
┌─────────────────────────────────────────────────────────────────┐
│                                  light energy                     │
│   The plants are used for food or fuel, and _____ and    │
│   _____heat energy_____ are released through chemical reactions.  │
└─────────────────────────────────────────────────────────────────┘
```

27. How can you make a chemical reaction happen faster or slower? <u>You</u>

<u>can control the rate of a chemical reaction by adding energy or taking it</u>

<u>away.</u>

CHAPTER 15, Changes in Matter *(continued)*

WordWise

The block of letters below contains 11 key terms from Chapter 15. Use the clues to identify the terms you need to find. Then find the terms across, down, or on the diagonal. Circle each term in the hidden-word puzzle.

Clues

The force exerted on a surface divided by the total area over which the force is exerted
_____ pressure _____

The change from the liquid to the gas state of matter
_____ vaporization _____

A state of matter with no definite shape or volume
_____ gas _____

A substance that can flow and easily change shape
_____ fluid _____

The resistance of a liquid to flowing
_____ viscosity _____

Vaporization that occurs on and below the surface of a liquid
_____ boiling _____

A state of matter that has no definite shape but has a definite volume
_____ liquid _____

The change in state from a liquid to a solid
_____ freezing _____

A state of matter that has a definite volume and a definite shape
_____ solid _____

The change in state from a solid to a liquid
_____ melting _____

A diagram that shows how two variables are related
_____ graph _____

v	a	p	o	r	i	z	a	t	i	o	n
i	u	r	l	m	l	i	q	u	i	d	f
s	s	e	n	e	y	q	i	d	x	g	r
c	o	s	o	l	i	d	w	n	n	r	e
o	w	s	m	t	p	f	f	i	p	a	e
s	x	u	m	i	a	s	l	d	d	p	z
i	t	r	c	n	a	i	c	u	p	h	i
t	t	e	g	g	o	x	c	i	i	x	n
y	c	i	p	b	t	w	q	m	c	d	g

© Prentice-Hall, Inc.

Science Explorer *Focus on Physical Science*

CHAPTER 16

ELEMENTS AND THE PERIODIC TABLE

· ·

SECTION 16–1 **Organizing the Elements** (pages 500–510)

This section explains how the elements are organized in a chart called the periodic table. It also explains what information the periodic table contains.

▶ **Looking for Patterns in the Elements** (page 500)

1. Is the following sentence true or false? All elements easily form

   compounds with other elements. _____false_____

▶ **Mendeleev, the Detective** (page 501)

2. What did Dmitri Mendeleev recognize in 1869? __He recognized a hidden__

   pattern in the elements.

3. What is the atomic mass of an element? __The atomic mass of an element__

   is the average mass of one atom of the element.

   _____

▶ **The First Periodic Table** (pages 501–502)

4. Mendeleev noticed that patterns appeared when he arranged the

   elements in what way? __Patterns appeared when he arranged the elements__

   in order of increasing atomic mass.

   _____

5. What does the word *periodic* mean? __Having a regular, repeated pattern__

   _____

CHAPTER 16, Elements and the Periodic Table *(continued)*

6. A chart of the elements showing the repeating pattern of their

   properties is called the _____ periodic table _____.

▶ The Periodic Table and the Atom (pages 502–505)

7. Circle the letter of each particle that is contained in the nucleus of an atom.

   (a.) proton   **b.** electron   **c.** period   **(d.)** neutron

Match the term with its definition.

Term	Definition
__c__ **8.** nucleus	**a.** Particles outside the nucleus
__e__ **9.** protons and neutrons	**b.** The number of protons in a nucleus
__a__ **10.** electrons	
__d__ **11.** atomic mass unit	**c.** The core of an atom
__b__ **12.** atomic number	**d.** A unit used in measuring particles in atoms
	e. Particles inside the nucleus

13. Is the following sentence true or false? Every atom of a particular

    element contains the same number of neutrons. _____ false _____

14. The modern periodic table is now arranged according to

    _____ atomic number _____.

▶ Reading the Periodic Table (pages 506–507)

15. A one- or two-letter representation of an element is called a(n)

    _____ chemical symbol _____.

16. Use the square from the periodic table to fill in the blanks below.

    Name of element: ___ Tin ___

    Chemical symbol: ___ Sn ___

    Atomic mass: ___ 118.710 ___

    Atomic number: ___ 50 ___

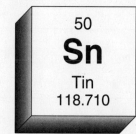

50

Sn

Tin

118.710

17. The atomic number for the element calcium (Ca) is 20. How many

protons and electrons does each calcium atom have? __Each calcium__

atom has 20 protons and 20 electrons.

_____

18. How can an element's properties be predicted? __An element's properties__

can be predicted from its location on the periodic table.

_____

19. Circle the letter of each term that refers to the elements in a column of
the periodic table.

    a. period   **(b.)** family   **(c.)** group   **d.** symbol

20. Group 15 of the periodic table is the ____nitrogen____ family.

21. Circle the letter of the statement that is true about elements in each group.

    a. They all have the same atomic mass.

    (b.) They all have similar characteristics.

    c. They all have similar atomic numbers.

    d. They all have the same chemical symbol.

22. Each horizontal row across the periodic table is called a(n)

____period____ .

23. Is the following sentence true or false? The elements in each period are

not alike in properties. ____true____

▶ Why the Table Works (pages 508–510)

24. What is bonding power? __It refers to the number of bonds an element__

forms during a chemical change.

_____

25. Electrons that are involved in sharing between or transfer to other

atoms are called ____valence electrons____ .

CHAPTER 16, Elements and the Periodic Table *(continued)*

26. Which electrons of an atom can be shared or transferred? _Only the_

    electrons that are farthest out can be shared or transferred.

27. Circle the letter of each sentence that is true about valence electrons.

    a. All elements have the same number of valence electrons.

    b. The number of valence electrons an element has increases from left to right across a period.

    c. The number of valence electrons determines whether the element gives up, shares, or accepts electrons.

    d. All elements in one group have the same number and arrangement of valence electrons.

 Reading Skill Practice

Writing a summary can help you remember the information you have read. When you write a summary, write only the most important points. Write a summary of the information under the heading *Reading the Periodic Table,* pages 506–507. Your summary should be shorter than the text on which it is based. Do your work on a separate sheet of paper.

Students' summaries should include definitions of the highlighted terms—chemical symbol, group, family, and period—as well as the main points under each subheading.

SECTION 16–2 **Metals** (pages 511-516)

This section describes the properties of metals and the characteristics of the different groups, or families, of metals.

▶ **What Is a Metal** (pages 511–512)

1. Chemists classify an element as a metal based on what physical

   properties? _Hardness, shininess, malleability, and ductility_

2. Is the following sentence true or false? Most metals are solids at room temperatures because they have the property of very low melting

   points. _false_

Match the term with its definition.

Term	Definition
<u>d</u> **3.** malleable	**a.** The ease with which an element combines with other elements and compounds
<u>c</u> **4.** ductile	**b.** A characteristic of those metals that are attracted to magnets or can be made into magnets
<u>b</u> **5.** magnetic	
<u>a</u> **6.** reactivity	**c.** A term used to describe a material that can be pulled out, or drawn, into a long wire
	d. A term used to describe a material that can be pounded or rolled into shape

7. Why are most metals called good conductors? They transmit heat and

electricity easily.

8. What is the gradual wearing away of a metal element called?

corrosion

▶ Alloys (page 513)

9. A mixture of metals is called a(n) alloy .

10. Bronze is a mixture of what two metals? copper and tin

▶ Families of Metals (pages 513–516)

11. How do the properties of each family of metals change as you move

across the table? The reactivity of the metals tends to decrease as you

move from left to right across the periodic table.

12. Circle the letter of each sentence that is true about alkali metals.

(a.) They are never found as elements but only in compounds.

(b.) Each atom of an alkali element has one valence electron that is easily transferred.

c. They are often found as pure elements in sea water.

(d.) They are extremely reactive.

CHAPTER 16, Elements and the Periodic Table *(continued)*

13. What are the two most important alkali metals?

sodium and potassium

14. Circle the letter of each sentence that is true about alkaline earth metals.

(a.) Each is a good conductor of electricity.

(b.) They are never found uncombined in nature.

(c.) They easily lose their valence electrons in chemical reactions.

d. They are much less reactive than most metals.

15. What are the two most common alkaline earth metals?

magnesium and calcium

16. Circle the letter of each element that is a transition metal.

(a.) gold　　　　**(b.)** iron　　　　**(c.)** copper　　　　**d.** lithium

17. Is the following sentence true or false? The transition metals are fairly

stable, reacting slowly or not at all with air and water. ___true___

18. What are the most familiar metals in groups 13 through 16? ___The most___

familiar are aluminum, tin, and lead.

_____

19. What is another name for the lanthanides and actinides?

rare earth elements

20. Where are the lanthanides and actinides found on the periodic table?

They are found at the bottom of the periodic table.

_____

21. Uranium has an atomic number of 92. How were all the elements with

atomic numbers higher than 92 created? ___They were created artificially in___

laboratories.

_____

22. Complete the concept map about metals.

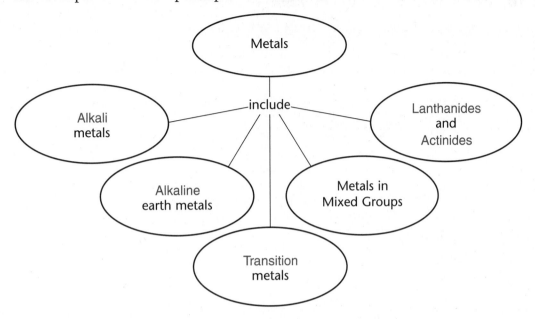

. . . .

SECTION 16-3 Nonmetals and Metalloids (pages 520-525)

This section describes properties of the elements on the periodic table that are not metals.

▶ What Is a Nonmetal (pages 520–521)

1. The elements that lack most of the properties of metals are called

   _____nonmetals_____ .

2. Where are the nonmetals found on the periodic table? __They are found__

   __to the right of the zigzag line.__

3. Is the following sentence true or false? Many of the nonmetals are gases

   at room temperature. _____true_____

4. Circle the letter of each sentence that is true about the physical
   properties of nonmetals.

   (a.) Solid nonmetals are brittle.

   (b.) They usually have lower densities than metals.

   c. Most are shiny.

   d. They are good conductors of both heat and electricity.

CHAPTER 16, Elements and the Periodic Table *(continued)*

5. Except for the Group 18 elements, most nonmetals readily form
   _____compounds_____.

6. What is a salt? __A salt is the product of a reaction between a metal and a__
   __nonmetal from Group 17.__

   _____

7. A molecule composed of two identical atoms is called a(n)
   _____diatomic molecule_____.

▶ Families of Nonmetals (pages 522–525)

8. Circle the letter of the number of valence electrons that an atom in the carbon family has.

   a. 1   **(b.)** 4   **c.** 5   **d.** 6

9. All living things contain what kind of compounds? __All living things__
   __contain compounds that are made of long chains of carbon atoms.__

   _____

10. Circle the letter of the number of valence electrons that an atom in the nitrogen family has.

    a. 2   **b.** 7   **(c.)** 5   **d.** 3

11. The atmosphere is almost 80 percent _____nitrogen gas_____.

12. Circle the letter of the number of valence electrons that an atom in the oxygen family has.

    (a.) 6   **b.** 7   **c.** 5   **d.** 2

13. Circle the letter of each sentence that is true about oxygen.

    (a.) The oxygen you breathe is a diatomic molecule.

    b. Oxygen rarely combines with other elements.

    (c.) Oxygen is the most abundant element in Earth's crust.

    (d.) Ozone collects in a layer in the upper atmosphere.

© Prentice-Hall, Inc.

14. Circle the letter of the number of valence electrons that an atom in the halogen family has.

    a. 4   **(b.)** 7   **c.** 6   **d.** 3

15. Is the following sentence true or false? Most halogens are dangerous to humans. _____true_____

16. Circle the letter of each sentence that is true about the noble gases.

    a. They exist in large amounts in the atmosphere.

    (b.) They are chemically very stable and unreactive.

    c. They readily share their valence electrons.

    (d.) They are used in glowing electric lights.

17. Complete the table about families of nonmetals.

Nonmetals		
Family	**Group**	**Nonmetals in Family**
Carbon family	Group 14	Carbon
Nitrogen family	Group 15	Nitrogen, phosphorus
Oxygen family	Group 16	Oxygen, sulfur, selenium
Halogen family	Group 17	Fluorine, chlorine, bromine, iodine
Noble gases	Group 18	Helium, neon, argon, krypton, xenon, radon

18. How many protons and electrons does a hydrogen atom contain?

A hydrogen atom contains only one proton and one electron.

19. Why can't hydrogen be grouped in a family? The chemical properties of hydrogen differ very much from those of the other elements.

CHAPTER 16, Elements and the Periodic Table *(continued)*

▶ The Metalloids (page 525)

20. What are metalloids? __They are elements that have some of the__ __characteristics of metals and some of the characteristics of nonmetals.__ _____

21. What is the most common metalloid? __silicon__

22. What is the most useful property of the metalloids? __Their most useful__ __property is their varying ability to conduct electricity.__ _____

23. What are semiconductors? __They are substances that under some__ __conditions can carry electricity, like a metal, while under other conditions__ __cannot carry electricity, like a nonmetal.__ _____

© Prentice-Hall, Inc.

SECTION 16–4	Elements From Stardust
	(pages 528-530)

This section explains how elements form inside stars.

▶ Atomic Nuclei Collide (pages 528–529)

1. Describe the plasma state of matter. __In the plasma state of matter,__ __atoms are stripped of their electrons and the nuclei are packed closely__ __together.__

2. The process in which atomic nuclei combine to form a larger nucleus, releasing huge amounts of energy, is called __nuclear fusion__.

3. What does nuclear fusion create inside stars? __heavier elements__

▶ Elements From the Sun (pages 529–530)

4. What is the major source of energy the sun now produces? __The sun's__

major source of energy is the nuclear fusion of hydrogen atoms.

_____

5. Complete the flowchart about nuclear fusion in stars.

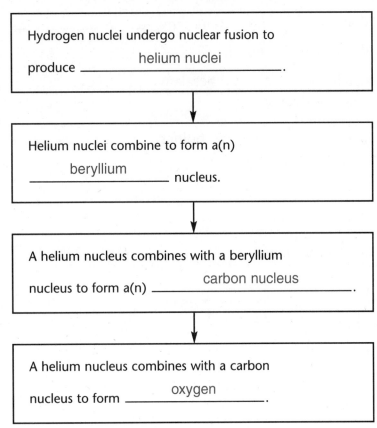

Hydrogen nuclei undergo nuclear fusion to

produce _____helium nuclei_____.

Helium nuclei combine to form a(n)

_____beryllium_____ nucleus.

A helium nucleus combines with a beryllium

nucleus to form a(n) _____carbon nucleus_____.

A helium nucleus combines with a carbon

nucleus to form _____oxygen_____.

▶ Elements from Large Stars (page 530)

6. In stars more massive than the sun, fusion continues until the core is

almost all _____iron_____.

7. What is a supernova? __It is a tremendous explosion that breaks apart a__

massive star.

_____

8. A supernova provides enough energy for the nuclear fusion reactions

that create the _____heaviest elements_____.

CHAPTER 16, Elements and the Periodic Table (continued)

WordWise

Use the clues to help you unscramble the key terms from Chapter 8. Then put the numbered letters in order to find the answer to the riddle.

Clues	Key Terms	
A tremendous explosion that breaks apart a massive star	eaousprnv	s u p e r n o v a (1 under p)
A term used to describe a material that can be pounded or rolled into shape	llbeealam	m a l l e a b l e (2 under e)
The gradual wearing away of a metal element	rsoooincr	c o r r o s i o n (3 under r, 4 under s)
A particle in the atomic nucleus that carries no charge	ouetnrn	n e u t r o n (5 under o)
A horizontal row across the periodic table	roiedp	p e r i o d (6 under d)
An element that has some characteristics of a metal and some characteristics of a nonmetal	ldmtioael	m e t a l l o i d (7 under i)
A term used to describe a material that can be drawn into a long wire	lecuitd	d u c t i l e (8 under u, 9 under c)
A state of matter in which atoms are stripped of their electrons and nuclei are packed close together	aamspl	p l a s m a (10 under s)
The elements in Group 18 of the periodic table	beoln ssgea	n o b l e g a s e s (11 under b)
Elements in the first row of the rare earth elements of the periodic table	sletahnaidn	l a n t h a n i d e s (12 under l, 13 under d)

Riddle: What chart shows the repeating properties of elements?

Answer: p e r i o d i c t a b l e
1 2 3 4 5 6 7 8 9 10 11 12 13

CHAPTER 17

CHEMICAL REACTIONS

....

SECTION 17-1 **Matter and Its Changes** (pages 536-541)

This section explains how you can tell when a chemical reaction has occurred. It also describes how chemical bonds are changed in reactions.

▶ Changes in Matter (pages 537-538)

1. What is chemistry? Chemistry is the study of the properties of matter and how matter changes.

2. What is a physical change? It is a change that alters the form or appearance of a material but does not make the material into another substance.

3. Is the following sentence true or false? A change of state is a physical change. ____true____

4. What is a chemical change? A chemical change is a change in matter that produces new substances.

5. Circle the letter of each sentence that describes a chemical change.

(a.) Two elements combine to make a compound.

(b.) A compound is broken down into elements.

c. A compound changes color but stays the same compound.

(d.) Two compounds change into other compounds.

CHAPTER 17, Chemical Reactions *(continued)*

6. A process in which substances undergo chemical change is called a(n)

_____chemical reaction_____.

▶ Observing Chemical Reactions (pages 538–539)

7. Is the following sentence true or false? You can never detect a chemical reaction just by observing changes in properties of matter.

_____false_____

8. A solid that forms from solution during a chemical reaction is called

a(n) _____precipitate_____.

9. What is the key characteristic of a chemical reaction? _____The key_____

characteristic is the production of new materials that are chemically different

from the starting materials.

_____

10. Use *Exploring Evidence for Chemical Reactions* on page 539 to complete the table.

Evidence for Chemical Reactions	
Type of Evidence	**Observed Evidence**
Color change	The color change of leaves in the fall
Precipitation	A precipitate forms when solutions are mixed
Gas production	Oxygen bubbles form on the leaves of an underwater plant
Changes in temperature	Water boils when placed on a natural-gas burner
Changes in properties	Soft dough changes into flaky bread in a hot oven

11. Are changes in properties always evidence for a chemical reaction?

Explain. <u>They aren't always evidence for a chemical reaction. For</u>

<u>example, when water changes state, its properties change. But a change of</u>

<u>state is a physical change, not a chemical change.</u>

_____

▶ Chemical Reactions on a Small Scale (pages 540–541)

12. Circle the letter of the sentence that is true about chemical reactions.

   a. Most chemical reactions involve only one step.

   b. A chemical reaction is a physical change of matter.

   c. Chemical reactions don't actually involve the particles of matter.

   (d.) A chemical reaction is the result of countless small changes.

13. How are chemical bonds involved in chemical reactions? <u>Chemical</u>

<u>reactions occur when chemical bonds are either formed or broken.</u>

_____

14. Why is glass unreactive? <u>Glass is unreactive because the chemical bonds</u>

<u>that hold it together are strong.</u>

_____

© Prentice-Hall, Inc.

· ·

SECTION 17-2 **Describing Chemical Reactions** (pages 544-551)

This section explains how to show chemical reactions with symbols. It also identifies three categories of chemical reactions.

▶ Introduction (page 544)

   1. What is a chemical equation? <u>A chemical equation is a shorter, easier</u>

<u>way to show chemical reactions, using symbols instead of words.</u>

_____

CHAPTER 17, Chemical Reactions (continued)

▶ Writing Chemical Equations (pages 545–546)

2. Most elements are represented by a one-letter or two-letter

_____symbol_____.

3. Use the table in Figure 6 on page 545 to write the symbol for each of the elements below.

a. Phosphorus _____P_____   **b.** Aluminum _____Al_____

c. Chlorine _____Cl_____   **d.** Sodium _____Na_____

e. Iron _____Fe_____   **f.** Silver _____Ag_____

4. A combination of symbols that shows the ratio of elements in a

compound is called a(n) _____chemical formula_____.

5. Use the table in Figure 7 on page 545 to write the chemical formula for each of the compounds below.

a. Ammonia _____NH_3_____   **b.** Baking soda _____$NaHCO_3$_____

c. Water _____H_2O_____   **d.** Carbon dioxide _____CO_2_____

e. Sodium chloride _____$NaCl$_____   **g.** Sugar _____$C_{12}H_{22}O_{11}$_____

6. What does a subscript show in a chemical formula? _A subscript shows_
the number of atoms of an element in a molecule. _____

_____

7. If a symbol in a chemical formula doesn't have a subscript, what is

understood about that symbol? _The number 1 is understood to be there._

_____

8. How many atoms of each kind of element are there in a molecule of

carbon dioxide (CO_2)? _A molecule of carbon dioxide has one carbon_

atom and two oxygen atoms. _____

_____

9. The materials you have at the beginning of a chemical reaction are

called ____reactants____.

10. The materials you have when a chemical reaction is complete are called

____products____.

11. What do you read the arrow in a chemical equation as meaning?

____yields____

12. Label each chemical formula in the chemical equation below as either a reactant or a product.

Fe	+	S	=	FeS
reactant		reactant		product

▶ Conservation of Mass (pages 546–547)

13. At the end of a chemical reaction, what is the total mass of the

reactants compared to the total mass of the products? ____The total mass____

of the reactants must equal the total mass of the products.

____

____

14. What is the principle called the conservation of mass? ____During a____

chemical reaction, matter is not created or destroyed.

____

____

▶ Balancing Chemical Equations (pages 547–548)

15. A number in front of a chemical formula in a chemical equation is

called a(n) ____coefficient____.

16. What does a coefficient tell you? ____It tells you how many molecules or____

atoms of each reactant or product take part in the reaction.

____

____

CHAPTER 17, Chemical Reactions *(continued)*

17. Tell why this chemical equation is not balanced: $H_2 + O_2 = H_2O$.

There are two oxygen atoms on the left side, but only one oxygen atom on

the right side.

_____

18. Write the balanced equation for this reaction: Oxygen reacts with

hydrogen to form water. $2\ H_2 + O_2 = 2\ H_2O$

▶ Classifying Chemical Reactions (pages 549–551)

19. How can chemical reactions be classified? Many chemical reactions can

be classified by what happens to the reactants and products.

_____

20. Complete the table about the three categories of chemical reactions.

Categories of Chemical Reactions		
Category	**Description**	**Example Chemical Equation**
Synthesis	Two or more substances combine to make a more complex compound.	$2\ SO_2 + O_2 + H_2O \longrightarrow 2\ H_2SO_4$
Decomposition	Compounds are broken down into simpler products.	$2\ H_2O_2 \longrightarrow 2\ H_2O + O_2$
Replacement	One element replaces another in a compound, or two elements in different compounds trade places.	$2\ CuO + C \longrightarrow 2\ Cu + CO_2$

21. Classify each of the following equations as synthesis, decomposition, or replacement.

a. $CaCO_3 \longrightarrow CaO + CO_2$ decomposition

b. $2\ Na + Cl_2 \longrightarrow 2\ NaCl$ synthesis

c. $Mg + CuSO_4 \longrightarrow MgSO_4 + Cu$ replacement

© Prentice-Hall, Inc.

Science Explorer *Focus on Physical Science*

SECTION 17-3 Controlling Chemical Reactions (pages 552-557)

This section explains how energy is related to chemical reactions. It also describes how the rate of a chemical reaction can be controlled.

▶ Energy in Chemical Reactions (page 553)

1. Is the following sentence true or false? Every chemical reaction involves a change of energy. ____true____

2. A reaction that releases energy in the form of heat is called a(n) ____exothermic reaction____.

3. A reaction that absorbs energy in the form of heat is called a(n) ____endothermic reaction____.

4. On the graph below, how does the energy of the products compare with the energy of the reactants? ____The energy of the products is higher than the energy of the reactants.____

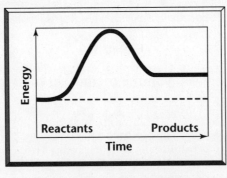

____Endothermic reaction____

5. Label the graph above as either an exothermic or endothermic reaction.

▶ Getting Reactions Started (pages 553–554)

6. What is the activation energy of a chemical reaction? ____It is the minimum amount of energy that has to be added to start a reaction.____

_____

CHAPTER 17, Chemical Reactions *(continued)*

7. What part of the graph in question 4 above represents the activation energy for the reaction? <u>The peak of the rise on the graph represents the</u> <u>activation energy.</u>

_____

8. In a reaction that makes water from hydrogen and oxygen, where does the activation energy come from? <u>An electric spark is the source of the</u> <u>activation energy. Then, the large amount of energy released by the reaction</u> <u>of the first few molecules provides the activation energy for more molecules</u> <u>to react.</u>

_____

▶ Rates of Chemical Reactions (pages 554–557)

9. What are three factors that affect the rate of a chemical reaction?

a. <u>concentration</u>

b. <u>surface area</u>

c. <u>temperature</u>

10. The amount of one material in a given volume of another material is called <u>concentration</u>.

11. To increase the rate of a reaction, why would you increase the concentration of the reactants? <u>Increasing the concentration of the</u> <u>reactants makes more particles available to react.</u>

_____

12. Circle the letter of each of the following that would increase the rate of a reaction.

(a.) Add heat.　　　　　　　　 b. Decrease the surface area.

(c.) Increase the surface area.　　 d. Reduce heat.

© Prentice-Hall, Inc.

13. What is a catalyst? _A catalyst is a material that increases the rate of a_

reaction by lowering the activation energy.

_____

14. Is the following sentence true or false? Catalysts are always permanently

changed in a reaction. _____false_____

15. A biological catalyst is called a(n) _____enzyme_____.

16. What is an inhibitor? _An inhibitor is a material used to decrease the rate_

of a reaction.

_____

📖 Reading Skill Practice

By looking carefully at illustrations in textbooks, you can help yourself understand better what you have read. Look carefully at Figure 16 on page 554. What important idea does this cartoon communicate? Do your work on a separate sheet of paper.

A chemical reaction is like a rock behind a ridge on top of a hill. There needs to be some energy exerted to get the rock over the ridge, just as there needs to be some activation energy to start a chemical reaction.

• •

SECTION 17-4 Fire and Fire Safety (pages 560-563)

This section describes the three things necessary to maintain a fire. It also explains how to prevent fires in the home.

▶ Understanding Fire (pages 560–562)

1. What is combustion? _Combustion is a rapid reaction between oxygen and_

a substance called a fuel.

_____

_____

CHAPTER 17, Chemical Reactions *(continued)*

2. A material that releases energy when it burns is called a(n)

_____fuel_____ .

3. What are the three things necessary to start and maintain a fire?

a. ___fuel_____   b. ___oxygen_____   c. ___heat_____

4. Circle the letter of where the oxygen for a fire comes from.

(a.) air   **b.** fuel   **c.** reactants   **d.** products

5. Is the following sentence true or false? An electric spark can provide the

activation energy needed to start a combustion reaction. _____true_____

6. How does water remove two parts of the fire triangle? ___Water covers the___

___fuel, which keeps it from coming into contact with oxygen. The evaporation of___

___water also uses a large amount of heat, causing the fire to cool.___

_____

▶ Home Fire Safety (pages 562–563)

7. What are four common sources of fires?

a. ___Small heaters_____

b. ___Fires in the kitchen_____

c. ___Faulty electric wiring_____

d. ___Carelessness with cigarettes_____

8. Circle the letter of each way to fight a fire.

a. Blow air on it.   (b.) Cover it with baking soda.

(c.) Use a fire extinguisher.   (d.) Pour water on it.

9. Circle the letter of each of the following that is a safety aid in a fire-safe home.

(a.) smoke detectors   **b.** gasoline can in the basement

(c.) fire extinguisher   (d.) box of baking soda in the kitchen

WordWise

Complete the sentences by using one of the scrambled terms below.

Word Bank

mocpsoinoited	dcsutrop	emtrsyhc	msubocniot	ysisehtns
lmheiacc lmrauof	ntreactonionc	etaptiicrpe	tyltsaac	ctatsnaer
nioatvicat	rtiohbiin	eaeeplcmnrt		

1. A material that increases the rate of a reaction by lowering the activation energy is called a(n) _____catalyst_____.

2. A chemical reaction that breaks down compounds into simpler products is called a(n) _____decomposition_____ reaction.

3. A solid that forms from solution during a chemical reaction is called a(n) _____precipitate_____.

4. The materials you have at the beginning of a chemical reaction are called _____reactants_____.

5. A chemical reaction in which two or more substances combine to make a more complex compound is called a(n) _____synthesis_____ reaction.

6. The amount of one material in a given volume of another material is called _____concentration_____.

7. A material used to decrease the rate of a reaction is called a(n) _____inhibitor_____.

8. A rapid reaction between oxygen and a fuel is called _____combustion_____.

9. The minimum amount of energy that has to be added to start a chemical reaction is called the _____activation_____ energy.

10. A chemical reaction in which one element replaces another in a compound, or in which two elements in different compounds trade places, is called a(n) _____replacement_____ reaction.

11. The substances formed as a result of a chemical reaction are called _____products_____.

12. A combination of symbols that shows the ratio of elements in a compound is called a(n) _____chemical formula_____.

13. The study of the properties of matter and how matter changes is called _____chemistry_____.

CHAPTER 17, Chemical Reactions *(continued)*

MathWise

Balance the chemical equations below by adding coefficients. Write the balanced equations on the lines below.

▶ Balancing Chemical Equations (pages 547–549)

1. $H_2O \longrightarrow H_2 + O_2$ $\quad \underline{2\ H_2O \longrightarrow 2\ H_2 + O_2}$

2. $N_2 + H_2 \longrightarrow NH_3$ $\quad \underline{N_2 + 3\ H_2 \longrightarrow 2\ NH_3}$

3. $NH_3 \longrightarrow N_2 + H_2$ $\quad \underline{2\ NH_3 \longrightarrow N_2 + 3\ H_2}$

4. $K + H_2O \longrightarrow H_2 + KOH$ $\quad \underline{2\ K + 2\ H_2O \longrightarrow H_2 + 2\ KOH}$

5. $Li + O_2 \longrightarrow Li_2O$ $\quad \underline{4\ Li + O_2 \longrightarrow 2\ Li_2O}$

6. $Fe + O_2 \longrightarrow Fe_2O_3$ $\quad \underline{4\ Fe + 3\ O_2 \longrightarrow 2\ Fe_2O_3}$

7. $Ag + N_2 \longrightarrow Ag_3N$ $\quad \underline{6\ Ag + N_2 \longrightarrow 2\ Ag_3N}$

8. $C_2H_5OH + O_2 \longrightarrow CO_2 + H_2O$ $\quad \underline{C_2H_5OH + 3\ O_2 \longrightarrow 2\ CO_2 + 3\ H_2O}$

CHAPTER 18

ATOMS AND BONDING

SECTION 18-1 **Inside an Atom** (pages 570-574)

This section describes the structure of an atom and explains the role that valence electrons play in forming chemical bonds.

▶ Structure of an Atom (pages 570–571)

1. What does an atom consist of? _An atom consists of a nucleus surrounded_

by one or more electrons.

_____

Match the particle with its charge.

____c____ **2.** neutron   **a.** positive

____a____ **3.** proton   **b.** negative

____b____ **4.** electron   **c.** neutral

5. Label the parts of an atom on the drawing.

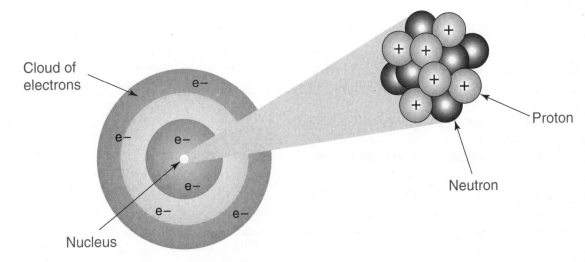

CHAPTER 18, Atoms and Bonding (continued)

6. Circle the letter of each sentence that is true about the parts of an atom.

    a. Protons are much lighter than electrons.

    b. The number of neutrons always equals the number of protons in a nucleus.

    (c.) In an atom, the number of protons equals the number of electrons.

    (d.) Neutrons have about the same mass as electrons.

▶ Electrons in Atoms (pages 571–574)

7. Where does most of the mass of an atom come from? _Most of the_ _____
   mass comes from the mass of the protons and neutrons. _____
   _____

8. The space in which the electrons move is huge compared to the space
   occupied by the _____nucleus_____.

9. What are the electrons farthest from the nucleus called?
   _____valence electrons_____

10. Circle each sentence that is true about valence electrons.

    (a.) The number of valence electrons an atom has determines whether or not the atom bonds with another atom.

    b. The valence electrons are the only electrons in the electron cloud.

    c. An atom's valence electrons help the other electrons form bonds with other atoms.

    (d.) Only valence electrons are involved in bonding.

11. A way to show the number of valence electrons an atom has, using dots
    around the symbol of an element, is a(n) _____electron dot diagram_____.

12. According to the dot diagram in Figure 3 on page 574, how many
    valence electrons does Argon (Ar) have? _Argon has eight valence_ ____
    electrons.

© Prentice-Hall, Inc.

▶ Why Atoms Form Bonds (page 574)

13. A chemical bond forms between two atoms when

_____ valence electrons _____ move between them.

14. What are two ways in which valence electrons move between atoms?

a. Electrons may be transferred from one atom to another. _____

_____

b. Electrons may be shared between the atoms. _____

_____

· ·

SECTION 18-2 Atoms in the Periodic Table (pages 575-577)

This section explains how the periodic table is organized. It also explains what the elements of each family have in common.

▶ Organizing the Elements (pages 575–576)

1. The number of protons in the nucleus of an atom is called the

_____ atomic number _____.

2. How are the elements arranged in the periodic table? __ They are _____

arranged from left to right and top to bottom in order of increasing atomic

number.

3. Complete the table by writing the definition of each term.

Organizing Elements	
Term	**Definition**
Group	The elements in a column of the periodic table
Family	The elements in a column of the periodic table
Period	A row of elements across the periodic table

CHAPTER 18, Atoms and Bonding (continued)

4. Is the following sentence true or false? The number of valence electrons increases from right to left across the periodic table. _____ false _____

5. Are the elements represented in Figure 6 on page 576 from a row across the periodic table or a column down the periodic table? ___They are from___ a row across the periodic table.

6. How many more valence electrons does a nitrogen atom have than a carbon atom? _____ one more _____

▶ Comparing Families of Elements (pages 576–577)

7. Circle the letter of the reason why each family in the periodic table has its own characteristic properties.

   (a.) Each element in a family has the same number of valence electrons.

   b. Each family shares its valence electrons among its elements.

   c. Each group has the same characteristics as a period.

   d. The periodic table begins with hydrogen.

8. Which group includes the noble gases? _____ Group 18 _____

9. Why are the noble gases also known as inert gases? ___Inert means___ inactive, and noble gases don't react very easily with other atoms.

   _____

10. The elements of Group 17 are also called the _____ halogen _____ gases.

11. Why does a fluorine atom react easily with other atoms that can give up electrons? ___A fluorine atom has seven valence electrons. The addition of___ just one electron will give it a more stable number of eight.

   _____

12. Why are elements in the halogen family very reactive? ___They each have___ seven valence electrons.

13. What property makes the alkali metals very reactive? _If alkali metals_ _lose one electron, the atoms are left with zero valence electrons, and they_ _become chemically stable._

14. Is the following sentence true or false? Hydrogen is extremely reactive. _____true_____

• •

SECTION 18-3 Ionic Bonds (pages 579-584)

This section explains how an atom becomes electrically charged. It also describes the characteristic properties of bonds formed by the attraction of electrically charged atoms.

▶ Electron Transfer (pages 579–580)

1. An atom or group of atoms that has become electrically charged is a(n) _____ion_____.

2. What happens to an atom when it loses an electron? _It loses a negative_ _charge and becomes a positive ion._

_____

3. What happens to an atom when it gains an electron? _It gains a_ _negative charge and becomes a negative ion._

_____

▶ Forming an Ionic Bond (pages 580–581)

4. What is an ionic bond? _An ionic bond is the attraction between two_ _oppositely charged ions._

5. Why does a sodium atom become more stable when it loses one valence electron? _It has only one, so when it loses that electron it has no more_ _electrons to form bonds with other atoms._

CHAPTER 18, Atoms and Bonding *(continued)*

6. What kind of ions do a sodium atom and a chlorine atom become when a valence electron is transferred from one to the other? ___The___ sodium atom becomes a positive ion, and the chlorine atom becomes a negative ion.

7. Use Figure 8 on page 580 to complete the table.

Ions and Their Charges		
Name	**Charge**	**Symbol or Formula**
Sodium	1+	Na^+
Magnesium	2+	Mg^{2+}
Chloride	1−	Cl^-
Sulfate	2−	SO_4^{2-}

8. What does the formula for the compound magnesium chloride, $MgCl_2$, tell you about how many chloride ions are needed to cancel out the charge of a magnesium ion? ___The formula shows that two chloride ions___ are needed to cancel out the charge of one magnesium ion.

▶ Polyatomic Ions (page 582)

9. Ions that are made of more than one atom are called ___polyatomic ions___.

10. How many atoms make up the carbonate ion (CO_3^{2-}), and what is its charge? ___It is made up of four atoms, including one carbon atom and three___ oxygen atoms. It has a charge of 2−.

▶ Naming Ionic Compounds (page 582)

11. Is the following sentence true or false? In an ionic compound, the name

of the negative ion comes first. _____*false*_____

12. When does the end of a name of a negative ion become *-ide*? ___*The end*___

becomes *-ide* when the negative ion is an element.

▶ Properties of Ionic Compounds (pages 583–584)

13. What are three characteristic properties of ionic compounds?

a. ___*crystal shape*___

b. ___*high melting points*___

c. ___*electrical conductivity*___

14. An orderly, three-dimensional arrangement formed by ions is called

a(n) ___*crystal*___.

15. In an ionic compound, every ion is attracted to what other ions? ___*They*___

are attracted to ions nearby that have an opposite charge.

16. At room temperature, ionic bonds are strong enough to cause all ionic

compounds to be ___*solids*___.

17. When do ionic compounds conduct electricity well? ___*They conduct*___

electricity well when they are dissolved in water.

 Reading Skill Practice

A flowchart can help you remember the order in which events occur. On a separate sheet of paper, create a flowchart that describes the steps that take place when sodium and chlorine atoms form an ionic bond. This process is explained in *Exploring Ionic Bonds* on page 581. For more information about flowcharts, see page 833 in the Skills Handbook of your textbook.

Students' flowcharts should begin with the transfer of one electron from the sodium atom to the chlorine atom.

CHAPTER 18, Atoms and Bonding *(continued)*

· ·

Covalent Bonds
(pages 585-589)

This section describes a chemical bond formed when two atoms share electrons. It also describes how electrons are shared unequally in some chemical bonds.

▶ **Electron Sharing** (page 585)

1. What is a covalent bond? __A covalent bond is a chemical bond formed__

    __when two atoms share electrons.__

2. On the dot diagram below, draw a circle around the shared electrons
   that form a covalent bond between two fluorine atoms.

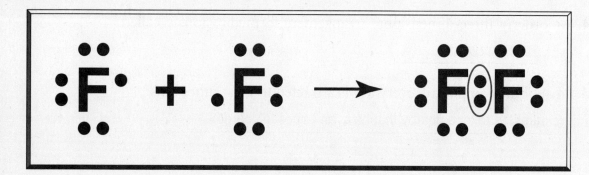

3. Circle the letter of the sentence that is true about a covalent bond in a
   molecule of fluorine.

    a. Only the right atom attracts the two electrons in the middle.

    b. Both atoms lose electrons.

    c. Both atoms attract the two shared electrons at the same time.

    d. Only the left atom attracts the two electrons in the middle.

▶ **How Many Bonds?** (page 586)

4. In the dot diagram of an oxygen molecule in Figure 13 on page 586, how

    many covalent bonds are in the molecule? _____two_____

5. A chemical bond formed when atoms share two pairs of electrons is

    called a(n) _____double bond_____.

▶ Properties of Molecular Compounds (pages 586–587)

6. What do molecular compounds consist of? _They consist of molecules_

having covalently bonded atoms.

_____

7. Circle the letter of each sentence that is true about molecular compounds.

a. More heat is needed to separate their molecules than is needed to separate ions.

(b.) They melt at much lower temperatures than do ionic compounds.

(c.) They boil at much lower temperatures than do ionic compounds.

(d.) They are poor conductors of electricity.

▶ Unequal Sharing of Electrons (pages 587–588)

8. How do molecular compounds come to have a slight electrical charge?

Some atoms pull more strongly on the shared electrons than other atoms

do. As a result, the electrons move closer to one atom, causing the atoms to

have slight electrical charges.

_____

9. In a polar covalent bond, electrons are shared _unequally_ .

10. How are electrons shared in a nonpolar covalent bond? _The electrons_

are shared equally.

_____

11. How can a molecule be nonpolar even when it has polar bonds? _A_

molecule is nonpolar if it contains polar bonds that cancel each other.

_____

12. Is the following sentence true or false? Water molecules are polar.

_____true_____

CHAPTER 18, Atoms and Bonding *(continued)*

▶ Attractions Between Molecules (pages 588–589)

13. Why do polar and nonpolar molecules have different properties? __The differences in attractions between molecules lead to the different properties.__

_____

14. Why don't water and vegetable oil mix? __Oil is nonpolar, and nonpolar compounds do not dissolve well in water. The polar water molecules are attracted more strongly to each other than to the molecules of oil.__

_____

15. When you do laundry, what causes the nonpolar dirt to mix with the polar water? __Detergent causes the dirt and water to mix.__

_____

. . . .

SECTION 18–5 Crystal Chemistry
(pages 592-594)

This section explains how chemical bonds are related to the properties of minerals.

▶ Mineral Properties (pages 592–593)

1. A naturally occurring solid that has a crystal structure and a definite chemical composition is called a(n) ____mineral____.

2. What properties do mineralogists use to identify minerals? __Color, shininess, density, crystal shape, hardness, and the way the mineral breaks apart__

_____

3. What do all the properties of a mineral depend on? __They all depend on its chemical composition.__

_____

Science Explorer *Focus on Physical Science*

▶ Bonding in Mineral Crystals (pages 593–594)

4. Is the following sentence true or false? All mineral crystals are made of

ions. _____false_____

5. What determines mineral properties such as crystal shape, hardness,

and the way the crystal breaks apart? _These properties are determined_

by the arrangement of particles in a mineral and the kind of bonds holding

them together.

_____

6. Complete the table about mineral crystals.

Mineral Crystals		
Type of Crystal	**How It Breaks**	**Example**
Ionic crystal	Splits along face of like charges	Halite
Covalent crystal	Breaks apart into irregular shapes	Quartz

▶ Comparing Crystals (page 594)

7. Is the following sentence true or false? The stronger bonds of quartz

make it harder than halite. _____true_____

8. If a mineralogist is in doubt about the identity of a mineral, what can he

or she do? _The mineralogist can test the sample for characteristics such as_

hardness and the way the crystals break.

_____

CHAPTER 18, Atoms and Bonding (continued)

WordWise

Answer the questions by writing the correct key terms in the blanks. Use the numbered letters in the terms to find the hidden key term. Then write a definition for the hidden key term.

Clues	Key Terms
What particles form a cloud around the nucleus of an atom?	e l e c t r o n s (1)
What is a covalent bond called in which electrons are shared unequally?	p o l a r (2)
_____ electrons are involved in bonding.	v a l e n c e (3)
What is an orderly, three-dimensional arrangement formed by ions called?	c r y s t a l (4)
What is the core of an atom?	n u c l e u s (5)(6)
What is an atom or group of atoms that has become electrically charged?	i o n (7)
What is the neutral particle in an atomic nucleus?	n e u t r o n (8)
What is the attraction between two oppositely charged ions called?	i o n i c b o n d (9)
What is a bond in which electrons are shared equally?	n o n p o l a r (10)
What is the positive particle in an atomic nucleus?	p r o t o n (11)
What is a bond in which two pairs of electrons are shared between atoms?	d o u b l e b o n d (12)

Key Term: c o v a l e n t   b o n d
              1 2 3 4 5 6 7 8   9 10 11 12

Definition: A chemical bond formed when two atoms share electrons

CHAPTER 19

ACIDS, BASES, AND SOLUTIONS

· ·

SECTION 19–1 **Working With Solutions** (pages 600–607)

This section explains what happens to particles of substances in solution. It also describes properties of solutions.

▶ Solutions and Suspensions (pages 600–601)

1. What is a suspension? __A suspension is a mixture in which particles can be__

__seen and easily separated by settling or filtration.__

_____

2. A well-mixed mixture is called a(n) _____solution_____.

3. Circle the letter of the mixture that is evenly mixed throughout.

   a. mixture   **(b.)** solution   **c.** suspension   **d.** compound

4. Circle the letter of each method you could use to separate salt from water.

   a. filtering   **(b.)** boiling   **(c.)** evaporation   **d.** settling

▶ Solvents and Solutes (pages 601–602)

5. Complete the table about solvents and solutes.

Parts of a Solution		
Part	**Definition**	**Which Part of Salt Water Solution?**
Solvent	The part of a solution present in the largest amount	Water
Solute	A substance present in a solution in a smaller amount	Salt

6. In a solution, the _____solute_____ is dissolved by the

   _____solvent_____.

CHAPTER 19, Acids, Bases, and Solutions *(continued)*

7. Why is water called the "universal solvent"? _Water is called that_

   because it dissolves so many substances. _____

   _____

8. According to the table in Figure 3 on page 602, what is the solute and

   what is the solvent in the solution called air? _Oxygen and other gases_

   are the solute; nitrogen is the solvent. _____

   _____

▶ Particles in a Solution (pages 602–603)

9. What happens to the solute's particles whenever a solution forms?

   The particles of the solute leave each other and become surrounded by

   particles of the solvent. _____

   _____

10. Circle the letter of each sentence that is true about particles in a solution.

    a. When an ionic solid mixes with water, its ions repel water molecules.

    (b.) When a molecular solid mixes with water, the covalent bonds are
    undisturbed.

    (c.) When an ionic solid mixes with water, water molecules surround
    each ion.

    d. When a molecular solid mixes with water, the solute's molecules
    break up.

▶ Concentration (page 603)

Match the term with its definition.

Term	Definition
_b_ **11.** dilute solution	**a.** A mixture that has a lot of solute dissolved in it.
_a_ **12.** concentrated solution	**b.** A mixture that has only a little solute dissolved in it.

▶ Solubility (page 604)

13. What is solubility? <u>Solubility is a measure of how well a solute can</u>

<u>dissolve in a solvent at a given temperature.</u>

14. A mixture that has so much solute in it that no more will dissolve is

called a(n) <u>saturated solution</u>.

15. A mixture in which more solute can be dissolved is called a(n)

<u>unsaturated solution</u>.

16. Which is more soluble in water, salt or sugar? <u>sugar</u>

▶ Changing Solubility (pages 604–605)

17. What are two factors that affect the solubility of a substance?

a. <u>temperature</u>   b. <u>type of solvent</u>

18. Circle the letter of each sentence that is true about temperature and
solubility.

(a.) Most solids become more soluble as the temperature goes up.

(b.) Most gases become less soluble as the temperature goes up.

c. Sugar dissolves better in cold water than in hot water.

(d.) Carbon dioxide dissolves better in cold water than in hot water.

19. Is the following sentence true or false? Ionic and polar compounds

dissolve in polar solvents. <u>true</u>

▶ Effects of Solutes on Solutions (pages 606–607)

20. Circle the letter of each sentence that is true about the effects of solutes
on solutions.

(a.) Solutes raise the boiling point of a solvent.

(b.) The temperature must drop lower than 0°C for water to freeze when
a solute is dissolved in the water.

c. Solutes raise the freezing point of a solvent.

d. Antifreeze boils at a lower temperature than pure water.

CHAPTER 19, Acids, Bases, and Solutions *(continued)*

··

SECTION 19-2 **Describing Acids and Bases**
(pages 610–615)

This section describes properties of compounds called acids and bases.

▶ **Properties of Acids** (pages 611–613)

1. What three properties are characteristic of an acid?

   a. It tastes sour.
   _____

   b. It reacts with metals and carbonates.
   _____

   c. It turns blue litmus red.
   _____

2. If you were a scientist, why wouldn't you use "sour taste" to identify a compound as acidic? Scientists never taste chemicals in order to identify them. Many acids are not safe to eat.
   _____

   _____

3. Why are acids often identified as corrosive? Acids eat away at other materials.
   _____

4. Complete the flowchart about etching.

   ┌───┐
   │ An artist coats a(n) ____metal plate____ with beeswax.│
   └───┘
                            ↓
   ┌───┐
   │ The artist cuts a design in the ____beeswax____,   │
   │ exposing the metal.   │
   └───┘
                            ↓
   ┌───┐
   │ When the plate is treated with a(n) ____acid____,   │
   │ the design forms on the metal.   │
   └───┘
                            ↓
   ┌───┐
   │ Later, ____ink____ applied to the plate collects in   │
   │ the grooves made by the acid.   │
   └───┘

5. What do carbonate ions contain? <u>They contain carbon and oxygen</u>

atoms bonded together.

6. What happens when acids react with compounds made of carbonates?

<u>A gas forms.</u>

7. What kind of rock is made of calcium carbonate?

    a. granite   **b.** sandstone   **c.** limestone   **d.** coal

8. What happens when a dilute solution of hydrochloric acid is poured on

a limestone rock? <u>Bubbles of carbon dioxide appear.</u>

9. Why would bubbles appear if an acid were poured on chalk? <u>Chalk is</u>

a form of limestone.

10. A compound that changes color in the presence of an acid or a base is

called a(n) <u>indicator</u>.

11. Why does lemon juice turn blue litmus paper red? <u>It turns blue litmus</u>

paper red because lemon juice is acidic.

_____

12. Is the following sentence true or false? Many of the vitamins in the foods

you eat are acids. <u>true</u>

13. Complete the table using information in Figure 13 on page 611 and in
Exploring Uses of Acids on page 613.

Common Acids		
Acid	**Formula**	**Use**
Hydrochloric acid	HCl	To clean bricks and metals
Nitric acid	HNO_3	To make fertilizers
Sulfuric acid	H_2SO_4	Used in batteries, to refine oil, and to treat iron and steel
Phosphoric acid	H_3PO_4	To make fertilizers

CHAPTER 19, Acids, Bases, and Solutions (continued)

▶ Properties of Bases (pages 614–615)

14. What three properties are characteristic of a base?

a. It tastes bitter. _____

b. It feels slippery. _____

c. It turns red litmus paper blue. _____

15. Why do your hands feel slippery when you rub soap on them under water?
Soap is a base, and bases feel slippery. _____

16. Is the following sentence true or false? Even a strong base can't hurt you
if you touch it. _____false_____

17. Is the following sentence true or false? A safe way to identify a base is to
feel it. _____false_____

18. Remembering the letter *b* will help you remember that
b__ases_____ turn litmus paper b__lue_____.

19. If a compound doesn't react with a metal or a carbonate, what do you
know about that compound? _____It isn't an acid._____

20. Complete the table using information in *Exploring Uses of Bases* on
page 614 and in Figure 15 on page 615.

Common Bases		
Base	**Formula**	**Use**
Sodium hydroxide	NaOH	In drain cleaners
Calcium hydroxide	$Ca(OH)_2$	In mortar and cement
Magnesium hydroxide	$Mg(OH)_2$	In medicines for stomach relief
Ammonia	NH_3	In household cleaning products
Calcium oxide	CaO	In mortar and cement and in soil additives

© Prentice-Hall, Inc.

• •

SECTION 19-3 **Acids and Bases in Solution**
(pages 616-621)

This section explains what kinds of ions acids and bases form in water. It also describes how the concentrations of ions are measured in a solution.

▶ Acids in Solution (pages 616–617)

1. What is a hydrogen ion (H^+)? __A hydrogen ion is an atom of hydrogen that__

__has lost its electron.__

_____

2. What do acids in water separate into? __hydrogen ions and negative ions__

_____

3. Any substance that forms hydrogen ions (H^+) in water can be called a(n)

_____acid_____.

▶ Bases in Solution (page 617)

4. What is a hydroxide ion (OH^-)? __A hydroxide ion is a negatively charged,__

__polyatomic ion made of oxygen and hydrogen.__

_____

5. Any substance that forms hydroxide ions (OH^-) in water can be called

a(n) _____base_____.

▶ Strengths of Acids and Bases (page 618)

6. Circle the letter of each sentence that is true about the strength of acids and bases.

   a. Strong bases produce more OH^- ions than weak bases.

   b. Weak acids produce more OH^- ions than strong acids.

   c. Strong acids produce more H^+ ions than weak acids.

   d. Weak bases produce more H^+ ions than strong bases.

CHAPTER 19, Acids, Bases, and Solutions *(continued)*

7. Circle the letter of each strong acid or strong base.

   a. ammonia   **b.** sulfuric acid   **c.** lye   **d.** citric acid

8. Is the following sentence true or false? A strong acid is safe as long as

   it's in a dilute solution. _____ false _____

▶ Measuring pH (pages 618–619)

9. What is the pH scale? __The pH scale is a range of values from 0 to 14. It__

   __expresses the concentration of hydrogen ions in a solution.__

   _____

10. On the scale below, add labels to show the pH of these substances: milk,
    soap, water, vinegar, lemon, and ammonia.

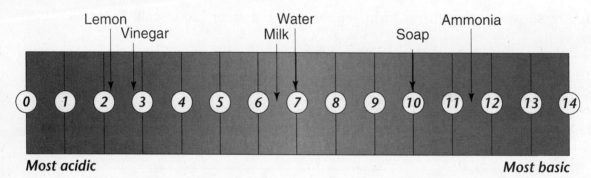

Most acidic   *Most basic*

11. When the pH of a solution is low, is the concentration of hydrogen ions

    high or low? _____ high _____

12. Circle the letter of each sentence that is true about pH.

    a. A pH lower than 7 is acidic.

    b. A pH of 7 is neutral.

    c. A pH lower than 7 is basic.

    d. A pH higher than 7 is acidic.

▶ Acid Rain (page 620)

13. Rain that is more acidic than normal rainwater is called

    _____ acid rain _____.

14. Why is acid rain a problem? It has a lower pH and is more corrosive
than normal rainwater. Acid rain can damage statues and buildings, destroy
forests, and kill fishes in lakes.

_____

▶ Acid-Base Reactions (page 620)

15. A reaction between an acid and a base is called a(n)
neutralization .

16. Is the following sentence true or false? An acid-base mixture is always
more acidic than the starting solutions were. false

▶ Products of Acid-Base Reactions (page 621)

17. What is a salt? A salt is any ionic compound that can form from the
neutralization of an acid with a base.

_____

18. What two substances does a neutralization reaction produce?

a. water _____

b. a salt _____

19. Circle the letter of the salt that is used as a de-icer for roads and
walkways.

    a. KCl   **b.** ammonium nitrate   **c.** $CaCO_3$ **(d.)** calcium chloride

---

📖 Reading Skill Practice

When you read about complex topics, writing an outline can help you organize and understand
the material. Outline Section 19–3 by using the headings and subheadings as topics and
subtopics of your outline and then writing the most important details under each topic. Do your
work on a separate sheet of paper.

Students' outlines should have seven major topics, matching the seven headings of the section.
Details should include all the highlighted key terms as well as the important concepts
discussed under each heading.

CHAPTER 19, Acids, Bases, and Solutions (continued)

· ·

SECTION 19-4 **Digestion and pH**
(pages 624-626)

This section explains why it is necessary for your body to digest food. It also explains how pH affects digestion.

▶ **What Is Digestion?** (pages 624–625)

1. The process that breaks down the complex molecules of food into

   smaller molecules is called _____digestion_____.

2. Why must foods be broken down in your body? __Your body can't use__

   foods in the forms in which you eat them. Foods must be broken down into

   simpler substances that your body can use for raw materials and energy.

   _____

3. Complete the table about the two processes of digestion.

Digestion	
Digestive Process	**Description**
Mechanical digestion	Tears, grinds, and mashes large food particles into smaller ones
Chemical digestion	Breaks large molecules into smaller molecules

4. What biological catalysts help chemical digestion take place?

   _____enzymes_____

5. Circle the letter of each sentence that is true about digestive enzymes.

   (a.) Enzymes require just the right temperature and pH to work.

   b. The pH must be neutral for enzymes to work.

   (c.) Some enzymes require the pH to be high.

   (d.) Some enzymes require the pH to be low.

▶ pH in the Digestive System (pages 625–626)

6. Is the following sentence true or false? The pH is not the same in all parts of the digestive system. _____true_____

7. What is amylase? ___Amylase is an enzyme in saliva that helps break down___ the carbohydrate starch into smaller sugar molecules. _____

8. Amylase works best when the pH is near _____7_____.

9. The stomach starts digestion of which kind of foods? ___It starts digestion___ of foods that contain protein, such as meat, fish, and beans. _____

10. What occurs in your stomach that drops the pH to a very acidic level of about 2? ___Cells in the lining of the stomach release solutions that include___ hydrochloric acid. _____

11. What does pepsin do? ___It breaks down proteins into small molecules___ called amino acids. _____

12. Pepsin works most effectively in _____acids_____.

13. What does food move into when it leaves the stomach? ___It moves into___ the small intestine. _____

14. Why does the pH in the small intestine rise to about 8? ___One digestive___ fluid in the small intestine contains the bicarbonate ion (HCO_3^-). _____

15. Is the following sentence true or false? Enzymes in the small intestine work best in a slightly basic solution. _____true_____

16. Most chemical digestion ends in the _____small intestine_____.

CHAPTER 19, Acids, Bases, and Solutions *(continued)*

WordWise

Match each definition in the left column with the correct term in the right column. Then write the number of each term in the appropriate box below. When you have filled in all the boxes, add up the numbers in each column, row, and two diagonals. All the sums should be the same.

A. A very well-mixed mixture

B. The part of a solution that is present in the smaller amount

C. A compound that changes color in the presence of an acid or a base

D. A substance that turns blue litmus paper red

E. A mixture that has a lot of solute dissolved in it

F. A negatively charged, polyatomic ion

G. A process that breaks down the complex molecules of food into smaller molecules

H. The part of a solution that is present in the larger amount

I. Any ionic compound that can form from the neutralization of an acid with a base

1. solute
2. digestion
3. hydroxide ion (OH⁻)
4. salt
5. concentrated solution
6. solution
7. acid
8. indicator
9. solvent

= 15

A 6	B 1	C 8	= 15
D 7	E 5	F 3	= 15
G 2	H 9	I 4	= 15
= 15	= 15	= 15	= 15

© Prentice-Hall, Inc.

CHAPTER 20

EXPLORING MATERIALS

· ·

SECTION 20–1 **Polymers and Composites** (pages 632–639)

This section explains how large, complex molecules form. It also describes properties of materials made of two or more substances.

▶ Carbon's Strings, Rings, and Other Things (page 633)

1. What do plastics and cells in your body have in common? _They are_

   made of carbon compounds. _____

   _____

2. Circle the letter of the number of covalent bonds that a carbon atom can form.

   a. 2   **b.** 3   (**c.**) 4   **d.** 5

▶ Carbon Compounds Form Polymers (page 633)

3. A large, complex molecule built from smaller molecules joined together

   is a(n) _____ polymer _____.

4. Describe three repeating patterns found in different polymers.

   a. _A single kind of monomer repeats over and over again._ _____

   _____

   b. _Two or three monomers join in an alternating pattern._ _____

   _____

   c. _Links between monomer chains occur, forming large webs or netlike_

   molecules. _____

CHAPTER 20, Exploring Materials *(continued)*

5. The smaller molecules from which polymers are built are called
   _____monomers_____.

▶ Natural Polymers (page 634)

6. Is the following sentence true or false? Living things produce the polymers
   they need from materials in the environment. _____true_____

7. What is cellulose? _____Cellulose is a flexible but strong natural polymer that_____
   gives shape to plant cells._____

8. Is the following sentence true or false? Your best wool sweater is made
   from natural polymers. _____true_____

9. In your body, proteins are polymers made from monomers called
   _____amino acids_____.

▶ Synthetic Polymers (page 635)

10. Complete the concept map about synthetic polymers.

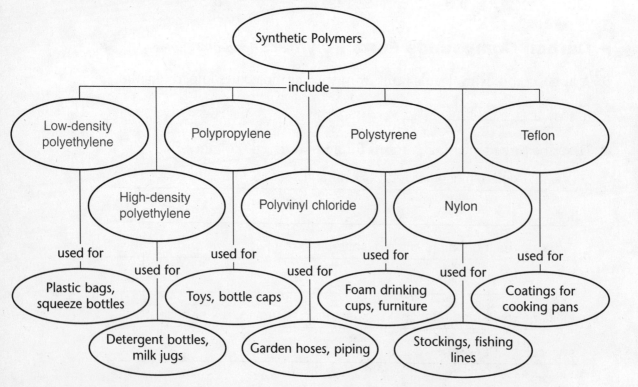

© Prentice-Hall, Inc.

11. The starting materials for most synthetic polymers come from
_____ .
              coal or oil

12. What are plastics? _Plastics are synthetic polymers that can be molded or_
shaped.

_____

13. Why are synthetic polymers often used in place of some natural materials?
The natural materials are too expensive or wear out too quickly.

_____

▶ **Composites** (pages 636–638)

14. What are composites? _Composites combine two or more substances as a_
new material with different properties.

_____

15. Why do chemists make composite materials? _By combining the useful_
properties of two or more substances in a composite, chemists can make a
new material that works better than either one alone.

_____

16. What are fiberglass composites composed of? _They are composed of_
strands of glass fiber that are woven together and strengthened with a liquid
plastic that sets like glue.

_____

▶ **Too Many Polymers?** (pages 638–639)

17. What are two disadvantages of using plastics? _It is often cheaper to_
throw away plastic materials and make new ones than it is to reuse them.

They don't break down into simpler materials in the environment.

_____

CHAPTER 20, Exploring Materials *(continued)*

18. What is one solution to solve the problems of plastics? _One solution is_

to use waste plastics as raw material for making new plastic products.

_____

_____

Reading Skill Practice

Writing a summary can help you remember the information you have read. When you write a summary, write only the most important points. On a separate sheet of paper, write a summary of Section 20–1. Your summary should be shorter than the text on which it is based.

Students' summaries should focus on the main points of each subsection and include bold-faced sentences and key terms.

SECTION 20-2 Metals and Alloys
(pages 643-647)

This section describes the properties of metals and substances made of two or more elements that are like metals.

▶ Introduction (page 643)

1. What is an alloy? _An alloy is a substance made of two or more elements_

that has the properties of metal.

_____

▶ Properties of Metals (page 643)

2. What are three properties of metals?

a. _They can conduct electricity._

b. _They can be drawn out into thin wire._

c. _They can be hammered into a sheet._

▶ Properties of Alloys (page 644)

3. How is bronze a better material than the elements that compose it?

Bronze is harder than either copper or tin, the elements that compose it.

4. Why are alloys used much more than pure metals? Alloys are generally

stronger and less likely to react with air or water.

5. Is the following sentence true or false? Gold alloys are much harder than

pure gold. _____ true

6. To make an airplane's "skin" strong, what is alloyed with aluminum?

Magnesium, copper, and traces of other metals are used.

7. Airplane turbine blades are made of nickel alloyed with iron, carbon, and cobalt. What properties does that alloy have that make it able to

do the job? It can spin around thousands of times per minute without

changing shape. It can also withstand temperatures up to 1,100°C.

▶ Making Alloys (page 644)

8. How have copper alloys been made since the beginning of the Bronze Age?

The metals are melted and mixed together in carefully measured amounts.

9. Circle the letter of two techniques used to make modern alloys.

    (a.) Firing a beam of ions at a metal

    b. Dipping the different elements in ice water

    (c.) Mixing the elements as powders and then heating them under high pressure

    d. Melting the metals and then spraying them onto another metal's surface

CHAPTER 20, Exploring Materials *(continued)*

▶ Using Alloys *(pages 645–647)*

10. What properties does high-carbon steel have that make it more useful

than wrought iron? High-carbon steel is stronger and harder than

wrought iron.

11. Is the following sentence true or false? There are only three types of

steel. _____ false _____

12. What elements make up the alloy used to fill a cavity in a tooth?

_____ mercury and silver or gold _____

13. Complete the Venn diagram to compare two types of steel.

Carbon Steel   **Stainless Steel**

Inexpensive

Used for tools,
knives, machinery

Hard and strong
alloys

Contain iron and
carbon

Resists corrosion

Used for tableware,
cookware, surgical
instrucments

Match the alloy with the elements that make it up.

Alloy

_b_ **14.** pewter

_c_ **15.** brass

_e_ **16.** sterling silver

_a_ **17.** stainless steel

_d_ **18.** carbon steel

Elements

a. Iron, carbon, nickel, chromium

b. Tin, antimony, copper

c. Copper, zinc

d. Iron, carbon

e. Silver, copper

19. What property does plumber's solder have that makes it useful for

sealing joints and leaks in metal plumbing? It has a low melting point.

© Prentice-Hall, Inc.

SECTION 20-3 Ceramics and Glass (pages 648-652)

This section describes the properties of solids made by heating clay and other minerals. It also explains how glass is made and used.

▶ Making Ceramics (pages 648–649)

1. Hard, crystalline solids made by heating clay and other materials to

   high temperatures are called _____ceramics_____.

2. How does a potter get the water out of clay used to make ceramic pottery?
   The potter heats the piece of pottery, and the water on the surface

   evaporates.

   _____

3. How does adding a glaze to a piece of pottery change the properties of

   the piece? __The glaze makes the piece of pottery shiny and waterproof.__

   _____

▶ Properties and Uses of Ceramics (pages 649–650)

4. Circle the letter of each property that makes ceramics useful.

   (a.) Ceramics do not conduct electricity.

   (b.) Ceramics resist moisture.

   c. Ceramics are brittle and can shatter when struck.

   (d.) Ceramics can withstand temperatures higher than those of molten
   metals.

5. Why are ceramic tiles used on the bottom of space shuttles?

   (a.) They withstand high temperatures.

   b. They protect against asteroids.

   c. They keep the shuttle waterproof.

   d. They let oxygen into the shuttle.

CHAPTER 20, Exploring Materials (continued)

6. What are three long-standing uses of ceramics?

a. roofing tiles _____ b. bricks _____ c. sewer pipes _____

▶ Making Glass (pages 650–651)

7. What is a clear, solid material with no crystal structure, created by

heating sand to a very high temperature? _____ glass _____.

8. Why did early glassmakers add limestone and sodium carbonate to

melting sand? __The mixture melts at a lower temperature than sand alone,__

so it is easier to work with.

▶ Communications Through Glass (pages 651–652)

9. What is an optical fiber? __An optical fiber is a threadlike piece of glass (or__

plastic) that can be used for transmitting light.

_____

10. Circle the letter of each material that optical fiber is replacing.

(a.) telephone lines   **b.** ceramic pipelines

c. ceramic tiles   (d.) cable television lines

· ·

SECTION 20-4 ## Radioactive Elements
(pages 653-659)

This section explains how radioactive elements change over time and describes how radioactive materials are used.

▶ Nuclear Reactions (page 654)

1. Why can't one element be made into another element by a chemical

reaction? __A chemical change always involves the electrons but does not__

affect the nucleus.

© Prentice-Hall, Inc.

2. What are nuclear reactions? _They are reactions involving the particles in_

the nucleus of an atom.

▶ Isotopes (page 654)

3. Atoms with the same number of protons and different numbers of

neutrons are called _____isotopes_____.

4. What is the mass number of an isotope? _The mass number is the sum of_

the protons and neutrons in the nucleus of the atom.

_____

5. What is the mass number of carbon-12? _____12_____

6. Circle the letter of the correct number of protons and neutrons that an
atom of carbon-14 has.

a. 7 protons and 7 neutrons

b. 14 protons and 14 neutrons

c. 6 protons and 8 neutrons

d. 8 protons and 6 neutrons

▶ Radioactive Decay (pages 654–655)

7. Is the following sentence true or false? The nucleus of an unstable atom

does not hold together well. _____true_____

8. What happens in the process called radioactive decay? _The atomic_

nuclei of unstable isotopes release fast-moving particles and energy.

_____

9. The particles and energy produced during radioactive decay are forms

of _____nuclear radiation_____.

10. Circle the letter of the type of nuclear radiation that is most
penetrating.

a. alpha particle   **b.** beta particle   **c.** gamma radiation   **d.** isotope

CHAPTER 20, Exploring Materials *(continued)*

11. Complete the table about radioactive decay.

Radioactive Decay		
Type of Radiation	**Description**	**Type of Radioactive Decay**
Alpha particle	Two protons and two neutrons	Alpha decay
Beta particle	One electron	Beta decay
Gamma radiation	High-energy waves	Gamma decay

12. Label each illustration below according to which type of radioactive decay it represents.

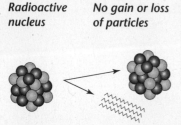  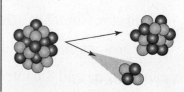

Radioactive nucleus	No gain or loss of particles	Radioactive nucleus	One less neutron, one more proton	Radioactive nucleus	2 protons and 2 neutrons lost

Gamma decay _____ Beta decay _____ Alpha decay _____

▶ Half-Life (page 656)

13. What is the half-life of an isotope? ___The half-life is the length of time___

needed for half the atoms of a sample to decay.

_____

14. Rank the following isotopes according to the length of their half-lives. Rank the isotope with the longest half-life as *1*.

___4___ iodine-131

___2___ carbon-14

___1___ uranium-238

___3___ cobalt-60

15. The process of determining the age of an object using the half-life of one or more radioactive isotopes is called _____radioactive dating_____.

▶ Using Radioactive Isotopes (pages 657–658)

16. What are tracers? __Tracers are radioactive isotopes that can be followed__ through the steps of a chemical reaction or industrial process.

17. How can biologists learn where and how plants use phosphorus? __They__ can add phosphorus-32 to the soil in which a plant is growing. Then they can use equipment that tracks the absorbed tracer through the plant.

18. How were the images made that are shown in Figure 24 on page 658? Technetium-99 was injected into the body. The isotope traveled to the lungs in one case and to the hand in the other case. Technicians made the images using equipment that detects radiation.

19. The process in which radioactive elements are used to destroy unhealthy cells is called _____radiation therapy_____.

20. What do nuclear power plants most often use as fuel?
    __uranium-235__

▶ Safe Use of Radioactive Materials (page 659)

21. How will dangerous radioactive materials be disposed of in the future? They will be placed in specially designed containers, which will be buried in very dry underground tunnels.

CHAPTER 20, Exploring Materials (continued)

WordWise

Solve the clues by filling in the blanks with key terms from Chapter 20. Then write the numbered letters in the correct order to find the hidden message.

Clues	Key Terms
A solid material with no crystal structure	<u>g</u> <u>l</u> <u>a</u> <u>s</u> <u>s</u> 　　　　　1
Synthetic polymers that can be molded and shaped	<u>p</u> <u>l</u> <u>a</u> <u>s</u> <u>t</u> <u>i</u> <u>c</u> <u>s</u> 　　　　2
A natural polymer that gives shape to plant cells	<u>c</u> <u>e</u> <u>l</u> <u>l</u> <u>u</u> <u>l</u> <u>o</u> <u>s</u> <u>e</u> 　　3　　　　　　4
The time needed for half the atoms of an isotope sample to decay	<u>h</u> <u>a</u> <u>l</u> <u>f</u> - <u>l</u> <u>i</u> <u>f</u> <u>e</u> 　　　　　5
Hard, crystalline solids made by heating clay and other materials	<u>c</u> <u>e</u> <u>r</u> <u>a</u> <u>m</u> <u>i</u> <u>c</u> <u>s</u> 　　　　　6
A combination of two or more substances that creates a new material	<u>c</u> <u>o</u> <u>m</u> <u>p</u> <u>o</u> <u>s</u> <u>i</u> <u>t</u> <u>e</u> 　　　　　7
A _____ reaction involves the particles in the nucleus of an atom.	<u>n</u> <u>u</u> <u>c</u> <u>l</u> <u>e</u> <u>a</u> <u>r</u> 　　　　　8
Small, carbon-based molecules	<u>m</u> <u>o</u> <u>n</u> <u>o</u> <u>m</u> <u>e</u> <u>r</u> <u>s</u> 　　　9
A radioactive isotope that can be followed through the steps of a chemical reaction	<u>t</u> <u>r</u> <u>a</u> <u>c</u> <u>e</u> <u>r</u> 　　　　10
A large, complex, carbon-based molecule	<u>p</u> <u>o</u> <u>l</u> <u>y</u> <u>m</u> <u>e</u> <u>r</u> 　　　11
The particles and energy produced during radioactive decay	<u>n</u> <u>u</u> <u>c</u> <u>l</u> <u>e</u> <u>a</u> <u>r</u> 　　　　12
	<u>r</u> <u>a</u> <u>d</u> <u>i</u> <u>a</u> <u>t</u> <u>i</u> <u>o</u> <u>n</u> 　　　　　　13
A process in which atomic nuclei of unstable isotopes release fast-moving particles and energy	<u>r</u> <u>a</u> <u>d</u> <u>i</u> <u>o</u> <u>a</u> <u>c</u> <u>t</u> <u>i</u> <u>v</u> <u>e</u> <u>d</u> <u>e</u> <u>c</u> <u>a</u> <u>y</u> 　　　　　14

Hidden Message

<u>S</u> <u>t</u> <u>e</u> <u>e</u> <u>l</u>　　<u>i</u> <u>s</u>　　<u>a</u> <u>n</u>　　<u>a</u> <u>l</u> <u>l</u> <u>o</u> <u>y</u>.
1　2　3　4　5　　6　7　　8　9　　10　11　12　13　14

CHAPTER 21

CHEMISTRY OF LIVING SYSTEMS

....

SECTION 21-1 Chemical Bonding, Carbon Style (pages 666-669)

This section explains why carbon can form a huge variety of different compounds. It also describes the different forms of pure carbon.

▶ **The Carbon Atom and Its Bonds** (page 667)

1. Circle the letter of the number of valence electrons a carbon atom has available for bonding.

   a. 2   **b.** 4   **c.** 6   **d.** 8

2. The transfer or sharing of valence electrons creates chemical _____bonds_____.

3. Is the following sentence true or false? Carbon atoms form more bonds than most other atoms. _____true_____

4. Circle the letter of the number of bonds each carbon atom is able to form.

   a. 2   **b.** 4   **c.** 6   **d.** 8

5. What are three ways carbon atoms bond to form the backbones for molecules?

   a. _straight chain_   **b.** _branched chain_   **c.** _ring_

▶ **Forms of Pure Carbon** (pages 668–669)

6. Why can the pure element of carbon exist in different forms? _It can exist in different forms because of the ways carbon forms bonds._ _____

_____

CHAPTER 21, Chemistry of Living Systems (continued)

7. Complete the table about forms of pure carbon.

Forms of Carbon			
Form	**Arrangement of Carbon Atoms**	**Properties**	**Use**
Diamond	Crystal structure	Extremely hard, unreactive	Gems, cutting tools
Graphite	Layers	Soft, slippery	Pencils, lubricants
Fullerene	Ball-shaped repeating pattern	Enclose an open area	Possibly hold medicine or computer circuits

8. Under what conditions do diamonds form? _____They form at very high_____

temperatures and pressures. _____

_____

9. How did fullerenes get their name? _____They were named after the architect_____

Buckminster Fuller, who designed geodesic domes. _____

· ·

SECTION 21–2 # Carbon Compounds
(pages 671–678)

This section describes the properties that many carbon compounds have in common. It also describes carbon compounds that contain only the elements carbon and hydrogen.

▶ Organic Compounds (pages 671–672)

1. Most compounds that contain carbon are called _____organic compounds_____

_____.

2. Why are many organic compounds liquid or gas at room temperature?

Organic compounds have low melting points and low boiling points. _____

_____

3. Circle the letter of each sentence that is true about organic compounds.

(a.) They generally have strong odors.

b. They have high boiling points.

(c.) Many don't dissolve well in water.

d. They are good conductors of electric currents.

▶ Hydrocarbons (pages 672–673)

4. What is a hydrocarbon? A hydrocarbon is a compound that contains only the elements carbon and hydrogen.

5. What are three carbon chains that form in hydrocarbons?

a. straight chains   **b.** branched chains   **c.** ring-shaped chains

6. Why are hydrocarbons used for fuel in stoves, cars, and airplanes?
Hydrocarbons release a great deal of energy when they burn.

7. A number in a molecular formula that tells you the number of atoms of an element in a compound is called a(n) subscript.

8. This is the molecular formula for a hydrocarbon called propane: C_3H_8.
What does this formula tell you about a molecule of propane? A molecule of propane contains three carbon atoms and eight hydrogen atoms.

▶ Straight Chains and Branches (page 674)

9. What does a structural formula show about a molecule of a compound?
It shows the kind, number, and arrangement of atoms in a molecule.

10. Each dash in a structural formula represents a chemical bond.

CHAPTER 21, Chemistry of Living Systems *(continued)*

11. The partially complete structural formula below shows the "backbone" for a propane molecule. Complete the structural formula of this hydrocarbon by showing all the hydrogen atoms that are bonded to the carbon chain.

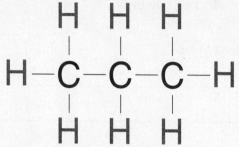

Propane (C₃H₈)

12. Compounds that have the same molecular formula but different structures are called ___isomers___.

▶ Double Bonds and Triple Bonds (page 675)

13. How do structural formulas represent a double bond in a molecule?

A double bond is represented with a double dash.

▶ Saturated and Unsaturated Hydrocarbons (page 675)

14. Complete the table about saturated and unsaturated hydrocarbons.

Saturated and Unsaturated Hydrocarbons			
Type of Hydrocarbon	**Bonds**	**Ending on Names**	**Example**
Saturated hydrocarbons	Single bonds	*-ane*	Ethane
Unsaturated hydrocarbons	Double or triple bonds	*-ene* or *-yne*	Acetylene

▶ Substituted Hydrocarbons (pages 676–677)

15. A hydrocarbon in which one or more hydrogen atoms have been replaced by atoms of other elements is called a(n)

substituted hydrocarbon

16. In compounds that contain halogens, what replaces hydrogen atoms?

One or more halogen atoms replace the hydrogen atoms.

17. Circle the letter of the hydroxyl group.

    a. –HO   **b.** –COOH   **(c.)** –OH   **d.** –COH

18. A substituted hydrocarbon that contains one or more hydroxyl groups

    is called a(n) _____alcohol_____.

19. Circle the letter of each alcohol.

    a. freon   **(b.)** ethane   **c.** acetic acid   **(d.)** methanol

20. Circle the letter of the carboxyl group.

    a. –HO   **(b.)** –COOH   **c.** –OH   **d.** –COH

21. A substituted hydrocarbon that contains one or more carboxyl groups

    is called a(n) _____organic acid_____.

▶ **Esters** (page 677)

22. An organic compound made by chemically combining an alcohol and

    an organic acid is called a(n) _____ester_____.

▶ **Polymers** (page 678)

23. What is a polymer? A polymer is a very large molecule made of a chain

of smaller molecules bonded together.

24. The smaller molecules that make up polymers are called

_____monomers_____.

25. What are synthetic polymers? They are polymers that are manufactured,

or synthesized, in factories.

CHAPTER 21, Chemistry of Living Systems *(continued)*

Reading Skill Practice

By looking carefully at illustrations in textbooks, you can help yourself better understand what you have read. Look carefully at Figure 11 on page 674. What important idea does this figure communicate?

The figure shows the structural and molecular formulas for two isomers. Although the molecular formulas are the same, the structural formulas are much different, which explains the different characteristics of butane and isobutane.

SECTION 21-3 Life With Carbon (pages 679–687)

This section describes the four main classes of polymers in living things.

▶ Nutrients From Foods (page 680)

1. Substances that provide the energy and raw materials the body needs to grow, repair worn parts, and function properly are called
   <u>   nutrients   </u>.

2. The process of breaking apart large molecules into small molecules is
   called <u>   digestion   </u>.

3. What are the four classes of polymers found in all living things?

   a. <u>carbohydrates</u>   b. <u>lipids</u>

   c. <u>proteins</u>   d. <u>nucleic acids</u>

▶ Carbohydrates (pages 680–682)

4. What is a carbohydrate? <u>A carbohydrate is an energy-rich organic</u>

   <u>compound made of the elements carbon, hydrogen, and oxygen.</u>

   _____

5. Circle the letter of the simplest carbohydrates.

   a. proteins   **b.** esters   **c.** sugars   **d.** hydrocarbons

© Prentice-Hall, Inc.

Science Explorer *Focus on Physical Science*

6. The sugar with the molecular formula of $C_6H_{12}O_6$ is called

_____glucose_____.

7. Why is glucose sometimes called "blood sugar"? __The body circulates__

glucose to all body parts through the blood.

_____

8. A long chain of simple carbohydrates is called a(n) __complex__

carbohydrate _____.

9. Complete the table about complex carbohydrates.

Complex Carbohydrates		
Type	**Description**	**Contained in These Foods**
Starch	A complex carbohydrate in which plants store energy	Bread, cereal, pasta, rice, potatoes
Cellulose	A complex carbohydrate that plants use to build strong stems and roots	Celery, fruit, vegetables, nuts

▶ Proteins (pages 682–683)

10. Polymers made of organic compounds called amino acids are

_____proteins_____.

11. Is the following sentence true or false? There are four different kinds of

amino acids. _____false_____

12. What elements make up amino acids? __They are made of carbon,__

nitrogen, oxygen, hydrogen, and sometimes sulfur.

_____

13. Circle the letter of each food that is a good source of protein.

    (**a.**)fish   (**b.**)beans   **c.** potatoes   (**d.**)meat

CHAPTER 21, Chemistry of Living Systems *(continued)*

14. What does the body use proteins for? It uses proteins to build and repair body parts.

▶ Lipids (pages 684–685)

15. What are lipids? Lipids are energy-rich polymers made of carbon, oxygen, and hydrogen.

16. What are four types of lipids?

a. fats   b. oils

c. waxes   d. cholesterol

17. Gram for gram, which stores more energy, lipids or carbohydrates?

lipids

18. What is each fat or oil molecule made of? Each fat or oil molecule is made of one short glycerol monomer and three long fatty acids.

19. A waxy lipid found in all animal cells is called _____ cholesterol _____.

▶ Nucleic Acids (page 686)

20. What are nucleic acids? Nucleic acids are very large organic molecules made up of carbon, oxygen, hydrogen, nitrogen, and phosphorus.

21. Complete the table about types of nucleic acids.

Nucleic Acids		
Common Name	**Full Name**	**Composed of**
DNA	Deoxyribonucleic acid	Four kinds of nucleotides
RNA	Ribonucleic acid	Four kinds of nucleotides

22. The monomers that make up nucleic acids are called

_____nucleotides_____ .

23. What do the differences among living things depend on? __They depend__

on the order of nucleotides in the DNA of each kind of living thing.

_____

24. Complete the flowchart about nucleic acids.

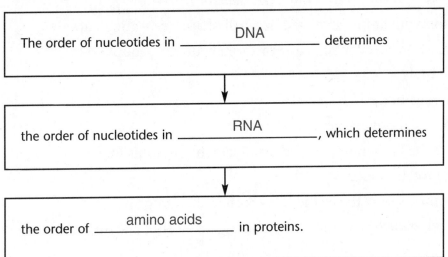

The order of nucleotides in _____DNA_____ determines

the order of nucleotides in _____RNA_____, which determines

the order of _____amino acids_____ in proteins.

▶ **Other Nutrients in Foods** (page 687)

25. Complete the table about other nutrients in foods.

Vitamins and Minerals		
Nutrient	**Definition**	**Examples**
Vitamins	Organic compounds that serve as helper molecules in a variety of chemical reactions	Vitamin C, Vitamin D
Minerals	Elements needed by your body	Sodium, calcium, iron, iodine, potassium

26. Is the following sentence true or false? You will probably get the vitamins and minerals you need if you eat a variety of foods.

_____true_____

CHAPTER 21, Chemistry of Living Systems (continued)

WordWise

Use the clues below to identify key terms from Chapter 21. Write the terms on the lines, putting one letter in each blank. When you finish, the word enclosed in the diagonal will reveal an important term related to the chemistry of living things. Define the term.

Clues

1. Substances that provide the energy and raw materials for the body
2. A form of pure carbon with atoms arranged in a ball-shaped repeating pattern
3. A substituted hydrocarbon that contains one or more hydroxyl groups
4. A sugar found in the body
5. Elements needed by your body
6. A –COOH group found in organic acids
7. A formula that shows the kind, number, and arrangement of atoms in a molecule
8. The monomers in a protein molecule
9. A compound that contains only the elements carbon and hydrogen
10. An organic compound made by chemically combining an alcohol and an organic acid

1. n u t r i e n t s
2. f u l l e r e n e
3. a l c o h o l
4. g l u c o s e
5. m i n e r a l s
6. c a r b o x y l   g r o u p
7. s t r u c t u r a l   f o r m u l a
8. a m i n o   a c i d s
9. h y d r o c a r b o n
10. e s t e r

Definition: A nucleotide is an organic compound that is one of the monomers of nucleic acids.

© Prentice-Hall, Inc.

CHAPTER 22

EARTH, MOON, AND SUN

© Prentice-Hall, Inc.

SECTION 22–1 **Earth in Space** (pages 704–711)

This section explains what causes day and night and what causes the cycle of seasons on Earth.

▶ Days and Years (pages 705–707)

1. The study of the moon, stars, and other objects in space is called

    _____astronomy_____.

Match the term with its definition.

	Term	Definition
_b_	2. axis	**a.** The movement of one object around another object
_d_	3. rotation	**b.** The imaginary line that passes through Earth's center and the North and South poles
_a_	4. revolution	**c.** The path of an object as it revolves around another object in space
_c_	5. orbit	**d.** The spinning motion of a planet around its axis

6. Each 24-hour cycle of day and night is called a(n) _____day_____.

7. Why is an extra day added to February every four years? _____Earth's orbit_____

    around the sun takes about 365¼ days. Four years of about 365¼ days each

    can be approximated by taking three years of 365 days and a fourth year of

    366 days.

    _____

CHAPTER 22, Earth, Moon, and Sun *(continued)*

8. What causes day and night? __Earth's rotation on its axis causes day and__ night.

▶ Seasons on Earth (pages 708–711)

9. Why is it warmer near the equator than near the poles? __It is warmer__ near the equator because sunlight hits Earth's surface directly and is less spread out at the equator.

_____

10. Why does Earth have seasons? __Earth has seasons because its axis is__ tilted as it moves around the sun.

_____

11. Circle the letter of each sentence that is true when the Northern Hemisphere has summer.

   (a.) The Southern Hemisphere is tilted away from the sun.

   b. The Northern Hemisphere is tilted away from the sun.

   c. The Southern Hemisphere is tilted toward the sun.

   (d.) The Northern Hemisphere is tilted toward the sun.

12. What is latitude? __Latitude is a measurement of distance from the equator,__ expressed in degrees north and south.

_____

13. Circle the letter of each sentence that is true about Earth's seasons.

   a. Earth is closest to the sun when it is summer in the Northern Hemisphere.

   b. The hemisphere that is tilted away from the sun has more daylight than the other hemisphere.

   (c.) When it is summer in the Northern Hemisphere it is winter in the Southern Hemisphere.

   (d.) In December, the sun's rays in the Northern Hemisphere are indirect.

14. Each of the two days of the year when the sun is overhead at either

    23.5° south or 23.5° north is called a(n) _____solstice_____.

15. Each of the two days of the year when neither hemisphere is tilted

    toward or away from the sun is called a(n) _____equinox_____.

16. Complete the table.

Earth's Seasons			
Day in Northern Hemisphere	**Approximate Date Each Year**	**Length of Daytime**	**Which Hemisphere Is Tilted Toward the Sun?**
Summer solstice	June 21	Longest daytime	Northern Hemisphere
Autumnal equinox	September 23	Daytime equals nighttime	Neither
Winter solstice	December 21	Shortest daytime	Southern Hemisphere
Vernal equinox	March 21	Daytime equals nighttime	Neither

SECTION 22-2 Phases, Eclipses, and Tides (pages 714-724)

This section explains what causes phases of the moon, what causes eclipses, and what causes the tides.

▶ Introduction (page 714)

1. What causes the phases of the moon, eclipses, and tides? _____These are all_____

   _____caused by the positions of the moon, Earth, and sun._____

▶ Motions of the Moon (pages 714–715)

2. Circle the letter of each sentence that is true about motions of the moon.

   a. The moon revolves around the Earth once a year.

   (b.) The "near side" of the moon always faces Earth.

   (c.) The moon rotates slowly on its axis once every 27.3 days.

   (d.) The moon's orbit around Earth is an oval shape.

CHAPTER 22, Earth, Moon, and Sun (continued)

▶ Phases of the Moon (pages 715–717)

3. The different shapes of the moon you see from Earth are called _____phases_____ .

4. How often does the moon go through a whole set of phases? __It goes__ through a whole set of phases each time it revolves around Earth, or about once a month.

5. What does the phase of the moon you see depend on? __It depends on__ how much of the sunlit side of the moon faces Earth.

6. Complete the table about phases of the moon.

Phases of the Moon	
Phase	**What You See**
New moon	Moon is dark.
First quarter	Half the moon is lighted.
Full moon	Whole side of the moon is lighted.
Third quarter	Half the moon is lighted.

▶ Eclipses (page 717)

7. When the moon's shadow hits Earth or Earth's shadow hits the moon, what occurs? __An eclipse occurs.__

8. What are the two types of eclipses?

a. __solar eclipse__   b. __lunar eclipses__

▶ Solar Eclipses (page 718)

9. The darkest part of a shadow is called the _____umbra_____ .

10. What happens to cause a solar eclipse? _The moon passes between_

Earth and the sun, blocking the sunlight from reaching Earth.

_____

11. The larger part of a shadow, surrounding the umbra, is called the

penumbra

_____ .

12. Circle the letter of each sentence that is true about solar eclipses.

    a. People in the umbra see only a partial solar eclipse.

    b. During a partial solar eclipse, part of the sun remains visible.

    c. During a total solar eclipse, the sky is dark.

    d. People in the penumbra see a total solar eclipse.

▶ Lunar Eclipses (page 719)

13. What is the arrangement of Earth, moon, and sun during a lunar

eclipse? _Earth is directly between the moon and the sun._

_____

14. Circle the letter of each sentence that is true about lunar eclipses.

    a. People in Earth's umbra see a total lunar eclipse.

    b. A lunar eclipse occurs at a full moon.

    c. During a lunar eclipse, Earth blocks sunlight from reaching the moon.

    d. A partial lunar eclipse occurs when the moon passes partly into the umbra of Earth's shadow.

▶ Tides (pages 722–724)

15. The rise and fall of the level of the ocean are called ____tides____ .

16. What force pulls the moon and Earth toward each other?

    ____gravity____

17. Why do tides occur? _Tides occur mainly because of differences in how_

much the moon pulls on different parts of Earth.

_____

CHAPTER 22, Earth, Moon, and Sun (continued)

18. Circle the letter of each sentence that is true about tides.

    (a.) The point on Earth that is closest to the moon has a high tide.

    b. Every location on Earth has two high tides per month.

    c. A low tide occurs at the point on Earth farthest from the moon.

    (d.) The water left behind at the point on Earth farthest from the moon has a high tide.

19. What is a spring tide? __A spring tide is a tide with the greatest difference__ between low tide and high tide.

20. What is a neap tide? __A neap tide is a tide with the least difference__ between low tide and high tide.

21. On each of the illustrations below, draw a moon to show its position at a spring tide and at a neap tide.

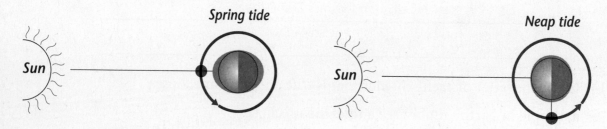

Spring tide   Neap tide

Sun   Sun

22. Circle the letter of each of the phases of the moon when a spring tide occurs.

    (a.) new moon   **b.** first quarter   **(c.)** full moon   **d.** third quarter

23. Is the following sentence true or false? Sometimes the effects of ocean tides extend far up rivers. _____true_____

 Reading Skill Practice

By looking carefully at illustrations in textbooks, you can help yourself understand better what you have read. Look carefully at Figure 6 on page 717. What important idea does this figure communicate?

It shows that the moon's orbit around Earth is slightly tilted with respect to Earth's orbit around the sun. As a result, in most months the moon revolves completely around Earth without moving into Earth's shadow or the moon's shadow hitting Earth.

SECTION 22-3 Rockets and Satellites (pages 725-728)

This section explains how rockets travel in space and describes what satellites and space stations are used for.

▶ How Rockets Work (page 725)

1. Why does a rocket move forward? __A rocket moves forward when gases expelled from the rear of the rocket push it in the opposite direction.__

2. For every force, or action, there is an equal and opposite force, or __reaction__ .

▶ Multistage Rockets (page 726)

3. How many stages do multistage rockets have? __three__

4. What happens to each stage when it uses up its fuel? __The empty fuel container drops off.__

5. What did the development of multistage rockets make possible? __Their development made it possible to send rockets to the moon and farther into space.__

▶ Artificial Satellites (pages 726–727)

6. What is a satellite? __A satellite is any natural or artificial object that revolves around an object in space.__

7. Circle the letter of the first artificial satellite launched into space.

   a. *Skylab*   **b.** *Explorer 1*   **c.** *Sputnik 1*   **d.** *Mir*

CHAPTER 22, Earth, Moon, and Sun *(continued)*

8. What are four uses of satellites and space stations?

a. communications   **b.** navigation

c. collecting weather data   **d.** research

9. What does it mean when a satellite is in a geosynchronous orbit? The satellite revolves around Earth at the same rate that Earth rotates.

10. Circle the letter of each sentence that is true about geosynchronous orbits.

(a.) They seem to hover over a given point on Earth.

b. People can live on them for long periods.

(c.) They are used to map weather patterns.

d. People can find them on Earth's surface.

11. A large satellite in which people can live for long periods is called a(n) space station .

12. What are the United States, Russia, and many other countries cooperating to build in space? the International Space Station

▶ Space Shuttles *(page 728)*

13. Why are space shuttles called "shuttles"? They can go back and forth, or shuttle, between Earth and space.

14. What would be the ideal vehicle to launch people and cargo into space? The ideal vehicle would be an aerospace plane that could take off from a runway, travel into space, and land again on a runway.

15. Is the following sentence true or false? Since 1981, space shuttles have been the main way that the United States launches astronauts and equipment into space. true

© Prentice-Hall, Inc.

SECTION 22-4 Earth's Moon (pages 729-734)

This section describes the features of the moon that can be seen with a telescope. It also describes the missions to the moon.

▶ The Structure and Origin of the Moon (page 730)

1. Circle the letter of the approximate size of the moon.

   a. about twice the size of Earth

   b. about half Earth's diameter

   c. about the size of Hawaii

   (d.) about one quarter Earth's diameter

2. Complete the flowchart about the collision theory of the moon's origin.

A Theory of the Moon's Origin

A large object strikes _____Earth_____.

↓

Material from _____Earth's_____ outer layer breaks off.

↓

The material from Earth is thrown into _____orbit_____.

↓

Material in orbit forms the _____moon_____.

▶ Looking at the Moon From Earth (pages 730–731)

3. Who made a telescope in 1609 that allowed him to see details of the

   moon nobody had ever seen before? _____Italian astronomer Galileo Galilei_____

_____

CHAPTER 22, Earth, Moon, and Sun *(continued)*

4. Name three features on the moon's surface.

   a. _craters_

   b. _highlands_

   c. _maria_

5. Round pits on the surface of the moon are called _____craters_____.

6. What are craters on the moon caused by? __They are caused by the__ impacts of meteoroids, rocks from space.

   _____

7. Circle the letter of the phrase that best describes maria.

   a. Highland peaks that cast dark shadows

   (b.)Low, dry areas that were once flooded with molten material

   c. Vast oceans that cover much of the moon

   d. Craters made from exploded volcanoes

▶ Missions to the Moon (pages 732–734)

8. Which president of the United States launched an enormous program of space exploration and scientific research in the early 1960s?

   President John F. Kennedy

9. Circle the letter of the spacecraft that flew into orbit around the moon in July, 1969.

   a. *Surveyor*   b. *Sputnik 1*   c. *Skylab*   (d.)*Apollo 11*

10. Who was the first person to walk on the moon? __*Apollo 11* astronaut__

    Neil Armstrong was the first to walk on the moon.

11. What did Neil Armstrong say when he took his first step onto the moon?

    That's one small step for man, one giant leap for mankind.

    _____

12. How have scientists learned about the material that makes up the moon's surface? _Much of what they have learned about the moon comes_ _from detailed study of the moon rocks gathered by astronauts._

13. How do scientists know that the moon's surface once was very hot? _Almost all of the moon rocks brought back by astronauts were formed from_ _the cooling of molten material._

14. What did scientists conclude from moon rocks that had been broken apart and then reformed? _Scientists concluded that meteoroids had_ _bombarded the moon's surface._

15. Is the following sentence true or false? The interior of the moon remains very hot. _false_

16. Is the following sentence true or false? Seismometers detected extremely strong moonquakes on the moon. _false_

17. Circle the letter of each sentence that is true about the far side of the moon.
   a. It is almost completely covered with maria.
   (b.) It is rougher than the near side.
   (c.) It has few maria.
   d. It is very smooth with no visible craters.

18. In 1998, what did the *Lunar Prospector* discover about the moon's poles? _It found evidence that there is ice frozen into the lunar soil near the moon's_ _poles._

CHAPTER 22, Earth, Moon, and Sun *(continued)*

WordWise

The hidden-word puzzle below contains 12 key terms from Chapter 22. You might find them across, down, or on the diagonal. Use the clues to identify the hidden terms. Then circle each term in the puzzle.

Clues	Key Terms
The spinning motion of a planet around its axis	rotation
The study of the moon, stars, and other objects in space	astronomy
The shapes of the moon you see from Earth	phases
The imaginary line that passes through Earth's center and the North and South poles	axis
The two days of the year on which the sun is directly overhead at either 23.5° north or south	solstice
Earth's path as it revolves around the sun	orbit
The movement of one object around another object	revolution
The rise or fall of the level of water in the ocean	tide
A round pit on the moon's surface	crater
The darkest part of a shadow	umbra
Dark, flat areas on the moon's surface	maria
The part of a shadow that surrounds the darkest part	penumbra

```
x   c   r   a   t   e   r   r   u   q   r
p   a   s   t   r   o   n   o   m   y   e
e   x   o   m   o   n   t   t   b   w   v
n   i   l   m   a   r   i   a   r   l   o
u   s   s   d   e   n   b   t   a   t   l
m   w   t   d   c   m   s   i   m   i   u
b   s   i   k   p   m   b   o   t   a   t
r   t   c   m   l   s   s   n   p   t   i
a   a   e   u   i   l   k   a   i   d   o
y   p   h   a   s   e   s   h   n   u   n
```

CHAPTER 23

THE SOLAR SYSTEM

....

SECTION 23–1 **Observing the Solar System** (pages 740-745)

This section describes the history of ideas about the solar system. It also explains the two factors that keep the planets in orbit around the sun.

▶ **Wandering Stars** (page 741)

1. What did the Romans name the five points of light that the Greeks called planets? _Mercury, Venus, Mars, Jupiter, and Saturn_ _____

_____

▶ **Greek Ideas: Earth at the Center** (page 741)

2. In a geocentric system, what is the arrangement of planets? _Earth is at_ _the center of the revolving planets._ _____

3. What was Ptolemy's explanation for why the planets seemed to move at different speeds? _He thought the planets moved on little circles that moved_ _on bigger circles._ _____

_____

▶ **Copernicus's Idea: Sun at the Center** (page 742)

4. A description of the solar system in which all the planets revolve around the sun is called a(n) _heliocentric system_ .

5. In the 1500s, who developed a heliocentric explanation for the motion of the planets? _Polish astronomer Copernicus_ _____

© Prentice-Hall, Inc.

CHAPTER 23, The Solar System (continued)

▶ Galileo's Observations (page 742)

6. What were two observations that Galileo made through his telescope
   that supported the heliocentric model? _He saw four moons revolving_
   around Jupiter and he discovered that Venus goes through phases similar to
   the moon's phases.

   _____

7. Circle the letter of whose ideas about the solar system are accepted today.

   a. Copernicus   **b.** the Greeks   **c.** Ptolemy   **d.** the Romans

▶ Brahe and Kepler (pages 742–743)

8. What is an ellipse? _An ellipse is an elongated circle, or oval shape._

   _____

9. Complete the table about Brahe and Kepler.

Brahe and Kepler			
Observer	**Time**	**Identification**	**Accomplishment**
Tycho Brahe	late 1500s	Danish astronomer	Observed the positions of the planets for almost 20 years
Johannes Kepler	1600	German mathematician	Discovered that the orbit of each planet is an ellipse

▶ Inertia and Gravity (pages 743–744)

10. What were the two factors Isaac Newton concluded that combined to
    keep the planets in orbit?

    a. _gravity_

    b. _inertia_

Science Explorer Focus on Physical Science

11. What is inertia? _Inertia is the tendency of a moving object to continue in_

a straight line or a stationary object to remain in place.

_____

12. Circle the letter of each statement that Newton made about the moon's orbit around Earth.

(**a.**)Earth pulls the moon toward it.

b. The moon keeps moving ahead because of gravity.

(**c.**)Earth curves away as the moon falls toward it.

(**d.**)Inertia keeps the moon moving ahead.

13. What does Figure 5 on page 744 show would happen if the force of

gravity didn't pull the planet toward the sun? _The planet would travel in_

a straight line away from the sun.

_____

14. Why are the planets in orbit around the sun? _The sun's gravity pulls on_

them while their inertia keeps them moving ahead.

_____

▶ **More to Discover** (page 745)

15. Astronomers still use telescopes to study the solar system. How have they

made even closer observations of the planets? _They have made close-up_

observations of the planets from space probes sent far into the solar system.

_____

 Reading Skill Practice

Writing a summary can help you remember the information you have read. When you write a summary, write only the most important points. On a separate sheet of paper, write a summary of the information in Section 23–1. Your summary should be shorter than the text on which it is based.

Students' summaries should be a short history of ideas about the solar system, including the ideas and discoveries of Ptolemy, Copernicus, Galileo, Brahe, Kepler, and Newton.

CHAPTER 23, The Solar System *(continued)*

• •

**SECTION
23-2** **The Sun**
(pages 746-750)

*This section describes the sun's interior and its atmosphere. It also describes features
on and above the sun's surface.*

▶ **The Sun's Interior** (pages 746-747)

1. The sun's energy comes from the process called _____nuclear fusion_____.

2. What occurs in nuclear fusion? ___Hydrogen atoms join together to form___
   ___helium atoms.___

3. Where does nuclear fusion occur on the sun? ___It occurs in the sun's___
   ___center, or core.___

4. What are three products of the nuclear fusion that occurs on the sun?

   a. ___helium___   b. ___light___   c. ___heat___

▶ **The Sun's Atmosphere** (pages 747-748)

5. Complete the table about the layers of the sun's atmosphere.

The Sun's Atmosphere		
Layer	**Description**	**When Is It Visible?**
Photosphere	The inner layer	When you look at an image or photograph of the sun
Chromosphere	The middle layer	At the beginning or end of a total eclipse
Corona	The outer layer	During eclipses or with special telescopes

6. The corona sends out a stream of electrically charged particles called

   ___solar wind___.

▶ Features on the Sun (pages 748–750)

7. What are three features on or above the sun's surface?

   a. sunspots   b. prominences   c. solar flares

8. Complete the table about features on the sun.

Features on the Sun	
Feature	**Description**
Sunspots	Areas of gas on the sun that are cooler than the gases around them
Prominences	Reddish loops of gas that connect different parts of sunspot regions
Solar flares	Explosions of hydrogen gas out into space

9. Short-term changes in climate on Earth may be related to

   _____ sunspot cycles _____.

10. When solar flares increase solar wind from the corona, what do they

    cause in Earth's upper atmosphere? _____ magnetic storms _____

• •

SECTION 23–3 The Inner Planets (pages 752-759)

This section describes the main characteristics of the four planets closest to the sun.

▶ Introduction (page 752)

1. Which planets are often called the terrestrial planets? _The inner

   planets—Mercury, Venus, Earth, and Mars_

   _____

2. What are two similarities among the inner planets? _They are small and

   have rocky surfaces._

   _____

CHAPTER 23, The Solar System *(continued)*

3. Look at the table in Figure 10 on page 753. Rank the inner planets according to diameter. Rank the planet with the greatest diameter as *1*.

   ___4___ Mercury   ___2___ Venus   ___1___ Earth   ___3___ Mars

4. Which planet rotates on its axis in about the same amount of time as Earth does? _____Mars_____

5. The drawing below shows the sun and the four inner planets. Label the inner planets according to their place in the solar system.

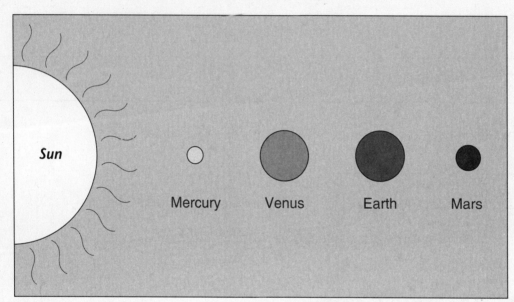

   Sun   Mercury   Venus   Earth   Mars

▶ **Earth** (pages 752–753)

6. Circle the letter of each sentence that is true about Earth.

   (a.) About 70 percent of its surface is covered with water.

   b. Its atmosphere extends about 1 kilometer above its surface.

   c. Most of the atmosphere is composed of oxygen gas.

   (d.) No other planet in the solar system has oceans like it.

7. What are the three main layers of Earth?

   a. __crust__   b. __mantle__   c. __core__

8. What is Earth's dense inner core made of? _____iron and nickel_____

9. How can studying Earth help scientists understand other planets?

They use what they know about Earth to make inferences about other

planets.

▶ Mercury (page 754)

10. Is the following sentence true or false? Most of the gases Mercury once

had in its atmosphere apparently escaped into space. _____ true _____

11. Circle the letter of each sentence that is true about Mercury.

(a.)Mercury's surface has many craters.

(b.)Mercury has no moons.

c. The interior of Mercury is composed mostly of the element mercury.

(d.)Mercury is the planet closest to the sun.

12. Why does Mercury have a greater range of temperatures than any other

planet? _____ It is so close to the sun that it gets very hot during the day. But

because it has almost no atmosphere, most of the heat escapes into space

at night, and the temperature becomes very cold.

▶ Venus (pages 755–757)

13. Because Venus is often a bright object in the west after sunset, it is

known as the _____ evening star _____.

14. Why is Venus sometimes called "Earth's twin"? _____ Venus is about the same

size as Earth.

15. Circle the letter of the gas that makes up most of the atmosphere of the
planet Venus.

   a. oxygen   **b.** nitrogen

   c. sulfuric acid   (**d.**)carbon dioxide

CHAPTER 23, The Solar System (continued)

16. Why is the rotation of Venus called retrograde rotation? __Venus rotates__

   from east to west, the opposite of the other planets.
   _____

   _____

17. Is the following sentence true or false? The atmosphere of Venus is so

   thick that it never has a sunny day. _____true_____

18. The trapping of heat by the atmosphere of Venus is called the

   _____greenhouse effect_____.

▶ Mars (pages 757–759)

19. Why is Mars called the "red planet"? __It has a slightly reddish tinge when__

   you see it in the sky.
   _____

   _____

20. The atmosphere on Mars is mostly _____carbon dioxide_____.

21. Is the following sentence true or false? There are no canals on Mars.

   _____true_____

22. Why do some regions on Mars look darker than others? __Wind storms__

   arise and blow the dust around on the surface of Mars. The darker regions
   _____

   are where the dust has been blown away.
   _____

   _____

23. Circle the letter of each sentence that is true about Mars.

   (a.) The rocks on Mars are covered with a rusty dust.

   (b.) Mars has seasons because it is tilted on its axis.

   c. Mars has many large oceans on its surface.

   (d.) Mars has giant volcanoes on its surface.

24. What are the two moons of Mars?

   a. __Phobos_____   b. __Deimos_____

● ●

SECTION 23-4 **The Outer Planets**
(pages 760-767)

This section describes the main characteristics of the five planets farthest from the sun. It also explains how Pluto is different from the other planets.

▶ Structure of the Gas Giants (pages 760–761)

1. The first four outer planets do not have solid _____surfaces_____.

2. Which four planets are known as the gas giants? ___Jupiter, Saturn, Uranus,___

   and Neptune

3. What is the composition of the atmospheres of the gas giants? ___Their___

   atmospheres are, on average, about 75 percent hydrogen, 24 percent helium,

   and 1 percent other elements.

   _____

4. Is the following sentence true or false? None of the gas giants has a

   solid surface, but all have a solid core. _____true_____

5. The drawing below shows the sun, the four inner planets, and the five outer
   planets. Label the outer planets according to their place in the solar system.

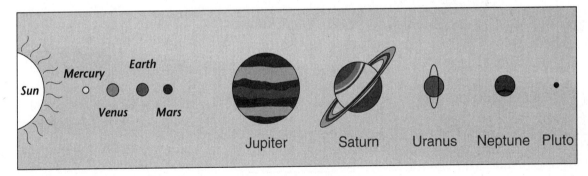

6. Why don't astronomers know much about the cores of the gas giants?

   The cores are buried so deep inside the gas giants that it has been hard to

   find out much about them.

   _____

CHAPTER 23, The Solar System (continued)

▶ Jupiter (pages 762–763)

7. Is the following sentence true or false? Jupiter's atmosphere is made up mainly of hydrogen and helium. _____true_____

8. What is the Giant Red Spot on Jupiter? __It is a giant area in Jupiter's__ atmosphere with swirling clouds many times bigger than Earth. It appears to be an ongoing storm similar to a hurricane on Earth.

9. Circle the letter of each sentence that is true about Jupiter.

   (a.) Jupiter's atmosphere contains many colorful bands.

   b. Jupiter's atmosphere is extremely thin.

   (c.) Jupiter has 17 moons revolving around it.

   (d.) Jupiter is the most massive planet in the solar system.

10. What are Jupiter's four largest moons?

    a. Ganymede _____   b. Callisto _____

    c. Io _____   d. Europa _____

11. Jupiter's moon Io is covered with _____volcanoes_____.

▶ Saturn (pages 763–764)

12. What are Saturn's rings made of? __They are made of chunks of ice and__ rock, each traveling in its own orbit around Saturn.

13. Is the following sentence true or false? Saturn has only 10 rings, although it looks like there are more. _____false_____

14. The largest of Saturn's 19 moons is called _____Titan_____.

▶ Uranus (page 765)

15. Why does Uranus look bluish? __It looks bluish because there are traces__ of methane in its atmosphere.

© Prentice-Hall, Inc.

16. What made astronomer William Herschel famous in 1781? <u>He</u>
<u>discovered the planet Uranus, the first planet discovered since ancient</u>
<u>times.</u>

17. How much larger is Uranus than Earth? <u>Uranus is about four times the</u>
<u>diameter of Earth.</u>

18. How is the rotation of Uranus unlike that of most of the other planets?
<u>Uranus rotates from top to bottom instead of from side to side, the way most</u>
<u>of the other planets do.</u>

19. How many moons does Uranus have? <u>17</u>

20. What are Uranus's five largest moons like? <u>They have icy, cratered</u>
<u>surfaces. They also have lava flows on their surfaces.</u>

▶ Neptune (page 766)

21. In the 1800s, why did astronomers predict that the planet Neptune
would be discovered well before anyone had seen it? <u>Uranus was not</u>
<u>quite following the orbit astronomers thought it should. They hypothesized</u>
<u>that the gravity of another planet was affecting Uranus's orbit.</u>

22. Circle the letter of the sentence that explains how the Great Dark Spot
was like the Great Red Spot.

    a. Both formed from volcanoes.   **b.** Both formed on rings.

    (c.) Both were probably storms.   **d.** Neither lasted long.

23. Is the following sentence true or false? Neptune's atmosphere is blue
and nearly featureless. <u>false</u>

24. Which is the largest of Neptune's eight moons? <u>Triton</u>

CHAPTER 23, The Solar System *(continued)*

▶ Pluto and Charon (page 767)

25. Is the following sentence true or false? Pluto is less than two thirds the

size of Earth's moon. _____ true

26. Why don't astronomers know much about Pluto and Charon? _____ They

are so far away that astronomers haven't been able to learn much about them.

_____

27. Circle the letter of each sentence that is true about Pluto.

a. Its moon is more than half Pluto's size.

b. Both Pluto and Charon have gaseous surfaces.

c. Astronomers often consider Pluto and Charon a double planet.

d. The American astronomer Clyde Tombaugh discovered Pluto in 1930.

28. Why do some astronomers think Pluto should not be called a planet?

It is so small that it may just be the largest of thousands of objects revolving

around the sun out beyond Neptune.

_____

. . . .

SECTION 23–5 Comets, Asteroids, and Meteors (pages 770-773)

This section describes the other objects in the solar system, including comets, asteroids, and meteors.

▶ Comets (pages 770–771)

1. What are comets? ___ Comets are chunks of ice and dust whose orbits are

usually very long, narrow ellipses.

_____

2. What are the three main parts of a comet?

a. nucleus _____ **b.** coma _____ **c.** tail _____

© Prentice-Hall, Inc.

Science Explorer *Focus on Physical Science*

3. How does a comet's tail form? Solar wind pushes the gas from a comet away from the sun. Gas and dust form the comet's tail.

4. Is the following sentence true or false? A comet's tail can be hundreds of millions of kilometers long. _____true_____

5. Who predicted that a comet would reappear in 1758? English astronomer Edmond Halley

▶ Asteroids (page 772)

6. Objects revolving around the sun that are too small and too numerous to be called planets are called _____asteroids_____.

7. Where is the asteroid belt? The asteroid belt lies between the orbits of Mars and Jupiter.

8. What happened when an asteroid collided with Earth 65 million years ago? Debris from the explosion probably started huge fires that destroyed much of Earth's forests and grass. As a result, many species became extinct, including the dinosaurs.

▶ Meteors (pages 772–773)

Match the term with its definition.

Term	Definition
_b_ **9.** meteoroid	**a.** A meteoroid that has passed through the atmosphere and hit Earth's surface
_c_ **10.** meteor	**b.** A chunk of rock or dust in space
_a_ **11.** meteorite	**c.** A streak of light caused by the burning up of a meteoroid in the atmosphere

CHAPTER 23, The Solar System (continued)

12. Where do meteoroids come from? <u>They usually come from comets or</u>

<u>asteroids.</u>

13. The craters on the moon were caused by the impact of

<u>meteoroids</u> .

• •

SECTION 23-6 **Is There Life Beyond Earth?**
(pages 774-777)

This section describes what conditions living things need to exist on Earth and explains why life might exist on Mars and Europa.

▶ **Introduction** (page 774)

1. Life other than that on Earth would be called <u>extraterrestrial life</u>

_____.

▶ **The "Goldilocks Conditions"** (pages 774–775)

2. What are the three "Goldilocks conditions" that Earth has that life as we know it needs to exist?

a. <u>liquid water</u>

b. <u>suitable temperature range</u>

c. <u>suitable atmosphere</u>

▶ **Life on Earth** (page 775)

3. Where has life been found on Earth that suggests that life forms can exist that do not need the "Goldilocks conditions"? <u>Life has been</u>

<u>found deep in the ocean, in caves, inside solid rocks, and in hot springs.</u>

_____

_____

Science Explorer *Focus on Physical Science*

▶ Life on Mars? (pages 776–777)

4. Why is Mars the most obvious place to look for living things like those

on Earth? Mars is the planet that is most similar to Earth.

_____

5. Why do scientists hypothesize that Mars may once have had the

conditions needed for life to exist? There are regions on Mars that were

almost certainly formed by flowing water. Life as we know it requires water to

exist.

_____

6. A meteorite from Mars found in Antarctica in 1996 shows tiny shapes

that look like _____fossils_____.

7. Is the following sentence true or false? All scientists agree that the
meteorite from Mars shows that life once existed on Mars.

_____false_____

8. What tested the soil of Mars for signs of life? A biology laboratory on a

Viking lander spacecraft.

9. Is the following sentence true or false? Life has been discovered in

Martian soil. _____false_____

▶ Life on Europa? (page 777)

10. What suggests that there might be liquid water on Europa? Close-up

views from *Galileo* show that Europa's ice has broken up and re-formed.

Similar patterns occur in the ice crust over Earth's Arctic Ocean.

_____

11. Is the following sentence true or false? If there is liquid water on Europa,

there might also be life. _____true_____

CHAPTER 23, The Solar System (continued)

WordWise

Answer the questions by writing the correct key terms in the blanks. Use the circled letters to find the hidden key term. Then write a definition for the hidden key term.

Clues

What is the middle layer of the sun's atmosphere?

p (h) o t o s p h (e) r e

What is an elongated circle, or oval shape, called?

e l (l) i p s e

What are the objects called that orbit the sun in a belt between Mars and Jupiter?

a s t e r o (i) d s

What is the spinning rotation of a planet from east to west called?

r e t r o g r a d e   r (o) t a t i o n

What is a description of the solar system in which all the planets revolve around Earth?

g e o (c) e n t r i c

What is a chunk of rock or dust in space called?

m e t (e) o r o i d

What are reddish loops of gas that connect different parts of sunspot regions?

p r o m i (n) e n c e s

What are areas of gas on the sun that are cooler than the gases around them?

s u n s p o (t) s

What is a stream of electrically charged particles sent out by the corona called?

s o l a (r)   w (i) n d

What is the outer layer of the sun's atmosphere?

(c) o r o n a

Key Term: h e l i o c e n t r i c

Definition: A description of the solar system in which all of the planets revolve around the sun

CHAPTER 24

STARS, GALAXIES, AND THE UNIVERSE

SECTION 24-1 **Tools of Modern Astronomy** (pages 784-790)

This section describes telescopes and other tools astronomers use to study the universe.

▶ Electromagnetic Radiation (page 785)

1. The light you see with your eyes is called _____ visible light _____.

2. What is electromagnetic radiation? _____ Electromagnetic radiation is energy _____

   that can travel directly through space in the form of waves. _____

   _____

3. The distance between the crest of one wave and the crest of the next

   wave is called the _____ wavelength _____.

4. A range of different wavelengths is called a(n) _____ spectrum _____.

5. What colors form the spectrum of visible light? _____ Red, orange, yellow, _____

   green, blue, and violet _____

6. What is the electromagnetic spectrum? _____ The electromagnetic spectrum is _____

   the range of wavelengths of electromagnetic waves. _____

   _____

7. What wavelengths are included in the electromagnetic spectrum? _____ It _____

   includes radio waves, infrared radiation, visible light, ultraviolet radiation, _____

   X-rays, and gamma rays. _____

   _____

CHAPTER 24, Stars, Galaxies, and the Universe *(continued)*

▶ Telescopes (pages 786–787)

8. What do most telescopes collect and focus? _They collect and focus_

different types of electromagnetic radiation, including visible light.

_____

9. What is a convex lens? _A convex lens is a piece of transparent glass,_

curved so that the middle is thicker than the edges.

_____

10. Complete the table about telescopes.

Telescopes	
Type	**Description**
Refracting telescope	A telescope that uses convex lenses to gather a large amount of light onto a small area
Reflecting telescope	A telescope that uses mirrors to focus a large amount of light onto a small area
Radio Telescope	A telescope that uses curved, reflecting surfaces to concentrate faint radio waves from outer space onto small antennas

11. What kind of telescope did Galileo use? _____refracting telescope_____.

12. The largest visible light telescopes are now all _____reflecting telescopes_____.

▶ Observatories (page 787)

13. A building that contains one or more telescopes is called a(n)

_____observatory_____.

14. Why have astronomers built the largest visible light telescopes on the

tops of mountains? _Earth's atmosphere makes objects in space look_

blurry. The sky on some mountaintops is clearer and is not brightened much

by city lights.

© Prentice-Hall, Inc.

▶ Satellites (page 788)

15. Why can the Hubble Space Telescope make images in visible light that

are much better than images made by telescopes on Earth? _It makes_____

better images because it is above Earth's atmosphere.

_____

_____

▶ Spectrographs (pages 789–790)

16. What does a spectrograph do? _A spectrograph breaks the light from an_

object into colors and photographs the resulting spectrum.

_____

17. What are two kinds of information that astronomers can collect from
stars by using spectrographs?

a. _chemical composition_____

b. _temperatures_____

18. Is the following sentence true or false? Each element has a unique set of

lines on a spectrum. _____true_____

19. How can astronomers infer which elements are found in a star? _They____

can compare a star's spectrum with the known spectrums of different

_elements._____

_____

20. Stars at different temperatures produce different ____line spectrums____.

21. How can astronomers infer how hot a star is? _They can compare a____

star's spectrum with the known spectrums of elements at different

_temperatures._____

_____

CHAPTER 24, Stars, Galaxies, and the Universe *(continued)*

SECTION 24-2 **Characteristics of Stars**
(pages 793-799)

This section explains how astronomers measure distances to stars. It also describes how stars are classified.

▶ **Introduction** (page 793)

1. A cluster of stars, gases, and dust held together by gravity is called a(n)
   _____galaxy_____.

2. What is the universe? __The universe is all of space and everything in it.__

   _____

3. Most of the universe is ____empty space____.

▶ **Distances to Stars** (page 794)

4. Complete the table about units of distance.

Units of Distance	
Unit	**Definition**
Astronomical unit	The average distance from Earth to the sun, about 150 million kilometers
Light-year	The distance light travels in one year, about 9.5 million million kilometers.

5. Is the following sentence true or false? The light-year is a unit of time.
   ____false____

▶ **Measuring Distances to Stars** (pages 794-795)

6. What is parallax? __Parallax is the apparent change in position of an object__

   __when you look at it from different places.__

   _____

© Prentice-Hall, Inc.

7. Circle the letter of what astronomers use parallax to measure the distance to.

   a. distant stars   **b.** the sun   **c.** the planets   **(d.)** nearby stars

8. To measure parallax shift, astronomers look at the same star twice, when Earth is on different sides of the _____ sun _____.

▶ Classifying Stars (page 795)

9. What are the three main characteristics used to classify stars?

   a. ___ size ___   **b.** ___ temperature ___   **c.** ___ brightness ___

▶ Sizes of Stars (page 796)

10. Stars that are much larger than the sun are called ___ giant stars ___.

11. Which kinds of stars are smaller than the sun?

   (a.) neutron star   **b.** giant star   **c.** supergiant star   **(d.)** white dwarf star

▶ Color and Temperature of Stars (page 796)

12. What reveals a star's temperature? ___ Its color reveals its temperature. ___

13. Circle the letter of what is revealed by the red color of the supergiant star called Betelgeuse.

   a. It is an extremely hot star.   **b.** It is in a constellation.
   c. It is far away.   **(d.)** It is a cool star.

▶ Brightness of Stars (pages 797–798)

14. The amount of light a star gives off is called its ___ brightness ___.

15. Why does Rigel shine as brightly as Betelgeuse, even though Rigel is much smaller than Betelgeuse? ___ Rigel is very hot and gives off a lot of light. Betelgeuse is a cool star, and doesn't give off much light. ___

CHAPTER 24, Stars, Galaxies, and the Universe (continued)

16. How bright a star looks from Earth depends on what two factors?

a. How far the star is from Earth

b. How bright the star actually is

17. Complete the table about the measurement of a star's brightness.

Brightness of Stars	
Measurement of Brightness	**Definition**
Apparent magnitude	A star's brightness as seen from Earth
Absolute magnitude	A star's brightness if it were a standard distance from Earth

18. Is the following sentence true or false? The closer a star is to Earth, the brighter it is. _____ true _____

19. What two things must an astronomer find out in order to calculate a star's absolute magnitude?

a. The star's apparent magnitude

b. The star's distance from Earth

▶ The Hertzsprung-Russell Diagram (pages 798–799)

20. The diagram that shows the relationship between the surface temperature and the brightness of stars is called the Hertzsprung-Russell diagram.

21. Look at the Hertzsprung-Russell diagram in Figure 10 on page 799. Write what is measured on each of the two axes of the diagram.

x-axis (horizontal axis): Surface Temperature (°C)

y-axis (vertical axis): Brightness

22. An area on the Hertzsprung-Russell diagram that runs from the upper left to the lower right and includes more than 90 percent of all stars is called the main sequence.

Science Explorer *Focus on Physical Science*

23. Circle the letter of each sentence that is true based on the Hertzsprung-Russell diagram.

a. The sun is a main-sequence star.

b. White dwarfs are brighter than supergiants.

c. Rigel is hotter than Betelgeuse.

d. Polaris is brighter than the sun.

 Reading Skill Practice

A flowchart can help you remember the order of steps in a process. On a separate sheet of paper, create a flowchart that describes the steps that astronomers use to measure the distance to stars, as described on pages 794–795. The first step in your flowchart should be: Astronomers look at a star when Earth is on one side of the sun. For more information about flowcharts, see page 833 in the Skills Handbook of your textbook.

Students' flowcharts should include the steps described in the text on pages 794–795 and Figure 6 on page 795.

· ·

SECTION 24-3 **Lives of Stars** (pages 802-806)

This section explains how the life of a star begins. It also explains what determines how long a star lives and what happens when a star runs out of fuel.

▶ **Introduction** (page 802)

1. A neutron star that gives off pulses of radio waves is called a(n)

_____pulsar_____.

▶ **Studying the Lives of Stars** (page 802)

2. Since astronomers can't study a single star for billions of years, how do

they know that stars go through stages in their lives? __Astronomers__

__study many stars and see how they differ from each other.__

_____

CHAPTER 24, Stars, Galaxies, and the Universe (continued)

▶ A Star Is Born (page 803)

3. A large amount of gas and dust spread out in an immense volume is called a(n) _____nebula_____.

4. Is the following sentence true or false? All stars begin their lives as part of nebulas. _____true_____

5. The earliest stage of a star's life is called a(n) _____protostar_____.

6. Describe how a star is born. _____A star is born when the contracting gas and_____ dust become so hot that nuclear fusion starts.

▶ Lifetimes of Stars (page 803)

7. Circle the letter of the factor that determines how long a star lives.
   (a.) its mass   **b.** its brightness   **c.** its volume   **d.** its temperature

8. Is the following sentence true or false? Stars with more mass last longer than stars with less mass. _____false_____

▶ Deaths of Stars (pages 804–806)

9. Complete the table by writing the definition of each term.

Deaths of Stars	
Term	**Definition**
White dwarf	The remaining hot core of a red giant after the outer part has drifted away
Black dwarf	A dead star after a white dwarf has run out of fuel
Supernova	An explosion of a red giant or supergiant
Neutron star	A tiny star that remains after a supernova
Black hole	The remains of a massive star pulled into a small volume by gravity

© Prentice-Hall, Inc.

Science Explorer *Focus on Physical Science*

10. Use the information in *Exploring the Lives of the Stars* on page 805 to complete the flowchart.

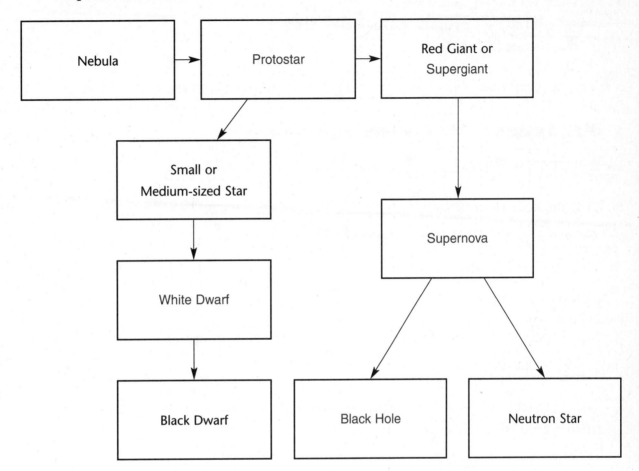

11. How do astronomers think the sun may have begun? __The sun may__

have begun as a nebula that contained material from a supernova

explosion.

12. Because no form of radiation can ever get out of a black hole, how can

astronomers detect where black holes are? __They can detect X-rays__

coming from rotating hot gas near a black hole. They can also calculate the

mass of a black hole from the effect of its gravity on a nearby star.

_____

13. A distant galaxy with a black hole at its center is called a(n)

_____quasar_____.

© Prentice-Hall, Inc.

CHAPTER 24, Stars, Galaxies, and the Universe (continued)

∙∙∙

SECTION 24-4 **Star Systems and Galaxies**
(pages 807-810)

This section explains what a star system is and describes the three types of galaxies.

▶ Star Systems and Planets (pages 807–809)

1. What are star systems? __They are groups of two or more stars.__

   _____

2. Star systems with two stars are called double stars or __binary stars__.

3. What does the double star Alpha Centauri A and Alpha Centauri B form

   with Proxima Centauri? __a triple star__

4. A star system in which one star blocks the light from another star is a(n)

   __eclipsing binary__.

5. Circle the letter of the correct explanation of how astronomers can tell if
   there is an unseen second star in a system.

   (a.) They observe the effects of its gravity.

   b. They measure the parallax of the second star.

   c. They send a probe to the second star.

   d. They observe its supernova.

6. How did astronomers deduce that the star called 51 Pegasi has a planet

   revolving around it? __They observed the effects of the planet's gravity on__

   __the star.__

▶ Galaxies (pages 809–810)

7. The galaxy in which our solar system is located is called the

   __Milky Way__.

8. How many galaxies are there in the universe? __billions__

9. On the drawing of the Milky Way Galaxy below, place a dot and write a label that shows where the sun is located.

Milky Way Galaxy

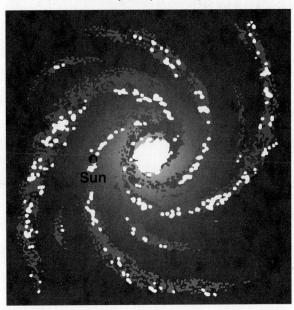

Sun

10. Complete the table about types of galaxies.

Types of Galaxies	
Type	**Description of Shape**
Spiral galaxies	Galaxies with arms that spiral outward, like pinwheels
Elliptical galaxies	Galaxies that look like flattened balls
Irregular galaxies	Galaxies that do not have regular shapes

11. For each galaxy below, write the type that it is.

Milky Way Galaxy: ___spiral galaxy_____

Large Magellanic Cloud: ___irregular galaxy_____

12. Circle the letter of each sentence that is true about galaxies.

a. Ellipitical galaxies contain only new stars.

b. There is lots of gas and dust between the stars in the Milky Way Galaxy.

c. The center of the Milky Way Galaxy is about 25,000 light years from the sun.

d. All galaxies have regular shapes.

CHAPTER 24, Stars, Galaxies, and the Universe *(continued)*

• •

SECTION 24–5   History of the Universe
(pages 811–814)

This section explains how astronomers think the universe and the solar system formed.

▶ Moving Galaxies (pages 811–812)

1. To study how and when the universe formed, what kind of information do astronomers use? <u>They use information about how galaxies are</u> <u>moving.</u>

2. Is the following sentence true or false? The further away a galaxy is from us, the faster it is moving away from us. <u>true</u>

3. How is the universe like rising raisin bread dough? <u>The galaxies in the</u> <u>universe, like the raisins in the bread dough, are moving away from each</u> <u>other. In the universe, it is space that is expanding, like the dough between</u> <u>the raisins.</u>

▶ The Big Bang Theory (pages 812–813)

4. The initial explosion that resulted in the formation and expansion of the universe is called the <u>big bang</u>.

5. When did the big bang occur? <u>It occurred about 10 to 15 billion years</u> <u>ago.</u>

6. From what can astronomers infer approximately how long the universe has been expanding? <u>They know approximately how fast the universe is</u> <u>expanding now.</u>

▶ **Formation of the Solar System** (pages 813–814)

7. Our solar system formed about _____ five billion years ago _____.

8. How did our solar system form? _____ A giant cloud of gas and dust, or nebula, _____

collapsed to form the solar system.

_____

_____

9. What events led to the birth of the sun? _____ The nebula shrank to form a _____

spinning disk. Gravity pulled some gas into the center of the disk, and the

gas became hot and dense enough for nuclear fusion to begin. Then the

sun was born.

_____

_____

▶ **The Future of the Universe** (page 814)

10. Describe two possibilities of what will happen to the universe in the future.

a. The universe will continue to expand until all the stars eventually run

out of fuel. Then the universe will be cold and dark.

_____

_____

_____

b. The force of gravity will begin to pull the galaxies back together. The result

will be a reverse big bang, or "big crunch." All of the matter of the universe

will be crushed into an enormous black hole.

_____

_____

CHAPTER 24, Stars, Galaxies, and the Universe (continued)

WordWise

Solve the clues by filling in the blanks with key terms from Chapter 24. Then write the numbered letters in the correct order to find the hidden message.

Clues	Key Terms
The earliest stage of a star's life	p r o t o s t a r 　　　1
The remains of a massive star pulled into a small volume by gravity	b l a c k　h o l e 　　　2
An instrument that breaks the light from an object into colors and photographs the resulting spectrum	s p e c t r o g r a p h 　　3
All of space and everything in it	u n i v e r s e 　　　　　4
A tiny star that remains after a supernova	n e u t r o n　s t a r 　　　5
The explosion that formed the universe	b i g　b a n g 　　　　　6
A pattern of stars in the sky	c o n s t e l l a t i o n 　　　　　　　7
The explosion of a dying giant or supergiant star	s u p e r n o v a 8
A galaxy that has a pinwheel shape	s p i r a l　g a l a x y 　　　9
A building that contains one or more telescopes	o b s e r v a t o r y 　　10
A device used to detect radio waves from objects in space	r a d i o　t e l e s c o p e 　　　　11
The apparent change in position of an object when you look at it from different places	p a r a l l a x 　　　12
A distant galaxy with a black hole at its center	q u a s a r 　　　　13

Hidden Message

T h e　s u n　i s　a　s t a r .
1 2 3　4 5 6　7 8　9　10 11 12 13